# Practice in the Basic Skills Mathematics 3

## Contents

| | | |
|---|---|---|
| **Number** | Addition | 2, 3, 7 |
| | Subtraction | 4, 5, 7 |
| | Notation | 6, 22 |
| | Multiplication | 8–14 |
| | Division | 15–21, 24 |
| | Number series and equations | 23 |
| **Fractions** | $\frac{1}{2}, \frac{1}{4}, \frac{1}{8}$ | 25, 26, 27 |
| | $\frac{1}{3}, \frac{1}{6}$ | 28 |
| | $\frac{1}{2}, \frac{1}{3}, \frac{1}{4}, \frac{1}{6}, \frac{1}{8}$ | 29 |
| | $\frac{1}{5}, \frac{1}{10}$ | 30 |
| | Problems | 31 |
| | Decimal notation | 32, 33 |
| | Decimal addition and subtraction | 34 |
| **Money** | Composition to £1·00 | 35, 36 |
| | Addition and subtraction | 37, 41 |
| | Multiplication and division | 38, 42, 43 |
| | Pounds and pence | 39, 40 |
| | Shopping problems | 44 |
| **Capacity** | 1 l, 500 ml, 250 ml, 125 ml | 45 |
| **Length** | m, cm and mm | 46, 47 |
| | km, m | 48 |
| | Perimeter | 48, 50 |
| | Area — cm² | 49, 50 |
| | Scale measurement | 51, 52 |
| **Mass** | kg and g | 53 |
| **Metric measures** | Problems | 54, 55 |
| **Time** | Minutes past and to | 56, 58, 59 |
| | am and pm | 57 |
| | Problems | 60 |
| | The calendar | 61 |
| **Graphs** | Vertical | 62 |
| | Horizontal | 63 |
| **Answers** | | 64–72 |

Published by Collins Educational
An imprint of HarperCollins*Publishers* Ltd
77-85 Fulham Palace Road
London W6 8JB

www.**Collins**Education.com
**On-line support for schools and colleges**

© Derek Newton and David Smith 2003
First published 1978
This edition published 2005 for Index Books Limited.

ISBN 0 00 775531 7

The authors assert the moral right to be identified
as the authors of this work.

British Library Cataloguing in Publication Data
A catalogue record for this book is available from
the British Library.

Illustrated by A Rodger

Printed in Thailand by Imago

# Revision — addition

| A | 40 | 46 | 32 | 26 | 33 | 84 | 53 |
|---|----|----|----|----|----|----|----|
|   | 26 | 11 | 26 | 51 | 42 | 13 | 41 |
|   | +12 | +22 | +31 | +22 | +14 | + 1 | + 4 |

| B | 264 | 251 | 871 | 524 | 749 | 410 | 555 |
|---|-----|-----|-----|-----|-----|-----|-----|
|   | 103 | 46 | 14 | 355 | 120 | 368 | 203 |
|   | +622 | +502 | +104 | +120 | + 30 | +210 | +121 |

| C | 45 | 32 | 85 | 49 | 24 | 63 | 52 |
|---|----|----|----|----|----|----|----|
|   | 27 | 28 | 9 | 18 | 49 | 26 | 17 |
|   | +26 | +27 | +15 | +13 | +29 | + 7 | +19 |

| D | 267 | 423 | 504 | 387 | 423 | 222 | 709 |
|---|-----|-----|-----|-----|-----|-----|-----|
|   | 108 | 347 | 264 | 207 | 67 | 548 | 159 |
|   | +519 | +216 | +225 | +204 | +408 | + 26 | +131 |

| E | 62 | 83 | 94 | 63 | 92 | 75 | 73 |
|---|----|----|----|----|----|----|----|
|   | 43 | 56 | 24 | 64 | 86 | 62 | 22 |
|   | +71 | +60 | +71 | +81 | +41 | +42 | +74 |

| F | 242 | 302 | 621 | 294 | 781 | 542 | 270 |
|---|-----|-----|-----|-----|-----|-----|-----|
|   | 70 | 482 | 193 | 182 | 192 | 333 | 477 |
|   | +635 | +172 | +154 | +292 | + 6 | + 84 | + 81 |

| G | 45 | 56 | 78 | 29 | 63 | 39 | 86 |
|---|----|----|----|----|----|----|----|
|   | 37 | 48 | 20 | 87 | 49 | 17 | 70 |
|   | +49 | +39 | +57 | +38 | +25 | +89 | +37 |

| H | 429 | 362 | 96 | 527 | 492 | 187 | 209 |
|---|-----|-----|-----|-----|-----|-----|-----|
|   | 76 | 249 | 287 | 209 | 271 | 483 | 385 |
|   | +147 | +158 | +402 | +186 | + 39 | +186 | +294 |

# Addition — thousands

**A**

| | | | | | |
|---|---|---|---|---|---|
| 331 | 127 | 236 | 624 | 842 | 705 |
| 840 | 931 | 543 | 601 | 724 | 632 |
| +526 | +341 | +820 | +253 | +413 | +252 |

**B**

| | | | | | |
|---|---|---|---|---|---|
| 247 | 538 | 867 | 328 | 835 | 424 |
| 726 | 227 | 278 | 305 | 347 | 657 |
| +485 | +993 | +654 | +770 | +562 | +206 |

**C**

| | | | | | |
|---|---|---|---|---|---|
| 909 | 722 | 474 | 200 | 742 | 526 |
| 236 | 337 | 826 | 439 | 758 | 437 |
| +474 | +560 | +658 | +527 | +214 | +485 |

**D**

| | | | | | |
|---|---|---|---|---|---|
| 862 | 925 | 720 | 536 | 453 | 304 |
| 604 | 859 | 673 | 950 | 822 | 957 |
| +973 | +980 | +858 | +707 | +968 | +983 |

**E**

| | | | | | |
|---|---|---|---|---|---|
| 425 | 739 | 729 | 651 | 945 | 472 |
| 808 | 716 | 937 | 614 | 867 | 870 |
| +802 | +528 | +462 | +939 | +445 | +763 |

**F**

| | | | | | |
|---|---|---|---|---|---|
| 510 | 954 | 865 | 697 | 896 | 482 |
| 827 | 927 | 794 | 485 | 813 | 958 |
| +735 | +483 | +978 | +891 | +824 | +761 |

**G**

| | | | | |
|---|---|---|---|---|
| 1431 | 2627 | 5003 | 9040 | 3214 |
| 2627 | 1393 | 2435 | 435 | 429 |
| + 431 | + 729 | +1620 | + 274 | +4005 |

**H**

| | | | | |
|---|---|---|---|---|
| 627 | 1109 | 2408 | 5406 | 643 |
| 5213 | 4329 | 770 | 603 | 7554 |
| +2471 | +3491 | +6378 | +2654 | +1500 |

# Revision — subtraction

| A | 963 | 899 | 764 | 869 | 427 | 588 |
|---|-----|-----|-----|-----|-----|-----|
| | −421 | −382 | −241 | − 53 | −306 | −337 |

| B | 974 | 659 | 432 | 784 | 904 | 747 |
|---|-----|-----|-----|-----|-----|-----|
| | −673 | − 58 | −331 | −482 | −503 | −346 |

| C | 843 | 978 | 503 | 726 | 298 | 629 |
|---|-----|-----|-----|-----|-----|-----|
| | −643 | −678 | −403 | −326 | −198 | −229 |

| D | 530 | 780 | 920 | 860 | 680 | 450 |
|---|-----|-----|-----|-----|-----|-----|
| | −217 | −358 | −416 | −345 | −257 | −139 |

| E | 607 | 908 | 306 | 505 | 403 | 804 |
|---|-----|-----|-----|-----|-----|-----|
| | −436 | −564 | −273 | −354 | −291 | −684 |

| F | 436 | 924 | 691 | 885 | 543 | 742 |
|---|-----|-----|-----|-----|-----|-----|
| | −227 | −508 | −479 | −466 | −225 | −334 |

| G | 539 | 428 | 917 | 646 | 354 | 866 |
|---|-----|-----|-----|-----|-----|-----|
| | −346 | −275 | −664 | −152 | −161 | −593 |

| H | 273 | 964 | 738 | 453 | 647 | 385 |
|---|-----|-----|-----|-----|-----|-----|
| | −178 | −676 | −459 | −288 | −279 | −287 |

| I | 300 | 700 | 600 | 800 | 500 | 900 |
|---|-----|-----|-----|-----|-----|-----|
| | −173 | −486 | −592 | −767 | −289 | −859 |

| J | 607 | 408 | 202 | 805 | 706 | 903 |
|---|-----|-----|-----|-----|-----|-----|
| | −488 | −139 | − 43 | −567 | −528 | −745 |

**K** Complete the number sentences.

$15 - \boxed{\phantom{0}} = 7$    $32 - 7 = \boxed{\phantom{0}}$    $32 + \boxed{\phantom{0}} = 41$    $\boxed{\phantom{0}} - 9 = 16$

$22 - \boxed{\phantom{0}} = 6$    $46 - 9 = \boxed{\phantom{0}}$    $16 + \boxed{\phantom{0}} = 23$    $\boxed{\phantom{0}} - 8 = 15$

$17 - \boxed{\phantom{0}} = 9$    $51 - 7 = \boxed{\phantom{0}}$    $18 + \boxed{\phantom{0}} = 31$    $\boxed{\phantom{0}} - 7 = 13$

# Subtraction — thousands

**A**

| 1047 | 1036 | 1029 | 1065 | 1054 | 1018 |
|------|------|------|------|------|------|
| − 523 | − 412 | − 908 | − 822 | − 741 | − 307 |

**B**

| 1276 | 1583 | 1469 | 1798 | 1657 | 1145 |
|------|------|------|------|------|------|
| − 540 | − 670 | − 825 | − 974 | − 710 | − 421 |

**C**

| 1859 | 1218 | 1736 | 1327 | 1145 | 1463 |
|------|------|------|------|------|------|
| − 976 | − 327 | − 853 | − 552 | − 871 | − 792 |

**D**

| 1157 | 1861 | 1618 | 1532 | 1423 | 1344 |
|------|------|------|------|------|------|
| − 258 | − 974 | − 949 | − 756 | − 648 | − 888 |

**E**

| 1008 | 1005 | 1004 | 1003 | 1002 | 1006 |
|------|------|------|------|------|------|
| − 359 | − 476 | − 528 | − 875 | − 736 | − 437 |

**F**

| 1000 | 1000 | 1000 | 1000 | 1000 | 1000 |
|------|------|------|------|------|------|
| − 435 | − 267 | − 875 | − 492 | − 814 | − 458 |

**G**

| 4027 | 7045 | 8089 | 2038 | 3067 | 6089 |
|------|------|------|------|------|------|
| −2471 | −5427 | −3947 | −1432 | −1745 | −2796 |

**H**

| 5386 | 4221 | 5167 | 9435 | 7549 | 9620 |
|------|------|------|------|------|------|
| −4827 | −2987 | −1496 | −3587 | −4592 | −4892 |

**I**

| 4000 | 7000 | 6000 | 3000 | 8000 | 5000 |
|------|------|------|------|------|------|
| −2532 | −3726 | −1847 | −2654 | −4359 | −4629 |

**J**

| 6005 | 4007 | 8006 | 3002 | 9005 | 7002 |
|------|------|------|------|------|------|
| −4739 | −2518 | −2929 | −1627 | −3426 | −6109 |

**K**  Write answers only.

| 62 minus 15 | 52 subtract 9 | 24 take 6 | 56 less 27 |
| 43 minus 8 | 27 subtract 18 | 61 take 34 | 23 less 14 |
| 32 minus 7 | 22 subtract 7 | 44 take 16 | 76 less 39 |

# Notation

**A** Write the value of the figure underlined in each number.

8027       435       3427       76       4232

6523       4231       9416       569       3410

**B** Write in figures

| | |
|---|---|
| six hundred and twenty | sixty |
| eight hundred and fifty | eighty-five |
| one hundred and fifteen | ninety |
| seven hundred and ten | two hundred |
| six thousand and fifty-four | forty-nine |
| three thousand and six | nine hundred and six |

**C** Write in words

4007       793       115       505       9620       20

30       402       530       107       3017       999

**D**

| | | | | |
|---|---|---|---|---|
| Add 1 to | 99 | 409 | 420 | 1199 |
| Take 1 from | 120 | 143 | 60 | 1230 |
| Add 10 to | 193 | 2290 | 186 | 993 |
| Take 10 from | 103 | 174 | 3077 | 706 |
| Add 100 to | 941 | 2304 | 1721 | 274 |
| Take 100 from | 572 | 2341 | 4831 | 2000 |

# Addition and subtraction

**A**  Write in columns then add.

47 + 276 + 3471

1347 + 23 + 547

2163 + 35 + 7

216 + 359 + 42 + 3129

4132 + 3671 + 26 + 9

8021 + 1021 + 104 + 15

741 + 603 + 1432 + 43

2916 + 356 + 7

2135 + 4236 + 17

4039 + 376 + 56

**B**  Write in columns then subtract.

4271 − 369                739 − 27

1402 − 347                496 − 171

8372 − 7                  2036 − 19

707 − 45                  3241 − 39

3271 − 2937              5436 − 207

4021 − 376               6271 − 499

**C**  Find the sum of 46, 325, 4216.

Find the total of 3216, 472, 27 and 9.

96 plus 376 plus 4298 plus 6.

To the sum of 46 and 217 add 767.

To 7421 add the sum of 96 and 432.

**D**  How much less than 2063 is 1479?

By how much is 734 greater than 529?

By how many is 76 less than 1006?

4326 minus 1023.

From 476 subtract 98.

# Multiplication — revision

**A**

| 424 | 112 | 122 | 333 | 322 | 212 |
|---|---|---|---|---|---|
| ×2 | ×3 | ×4 | ×3 | ×3 | ×4 |
| **848** | | | | | |

**B**

| 102 | 107 | 208 | 309 | 206 | 106 |
|---|---|---|---|---|---|
| ×5 | ×6 | ×4 | ×2 | ×3 | ×6 |
| **510** | | | | | |

**C**

| 227 | 346 | 119 | 115 | 117 | 124 |
|---|---|---|---|---|---|
| ×3 | ×2 | ×5 | ×6 | ×5 | ×4 |

**D**

| 390 | 151 | 172 | 191 | 182 | 283 |
|---|---|---|---|---|---|
| ×2 | ×6 | ×4 | ×5 | ×4 | ×3 |
| **780** | | | | | |

**E**

| 97 | 234 | 498 | 189 | 219 | 89 |
|---|---|---|---|---|---|
| ×6 | ×3 | ×2 | ×5 | ×4 | ×6 |

**F**

| 425 | 370 | 293 | 746 | 598 | 649 |
|---|---|---|---|---|---|
| ×6 | ×5 | ×4 | ×3 | ×2 | ×6 |

**G**

| 1471 | 2362 | 1625 | 1063 | 1549 |
|---|---|---|---|---|
| ×5 | ×3 | ×4 | ×6 | ×2 |

**H**

| 1361 × 4 | 1403 × 5 | 2347 × 2 | 1940 × 3 |
|---|---|---|---|
| 796 × 6 | 1079 × 5 | 3499 × 2 | 999 × 6 |

**I**   Multiply 276 by 5.          Find the product of 76 and 5.
    Multiply 1274 by 4.         Find the product of 143 and 4.
    Multiply 396 by 6.          Find the product of 98 and 6.

**J**   What number is three times two hundred and five?
    Multiply three hundred and fifty by four.
    Multiply together six and ninety-six.

# Multiplication by 7

**A**

$3 \times 7 = 21$   $7 \times 2 = 14$   $4 \times 7 = 28$   $7 \times 6 = 42$   $9 \times 7 = 63$

$12 \times 7 = 84$   $5 \times 7 = 35$   $8 \times 7 = 56$   $7 \times 3 = 21$   $2 \times 7 = 14$

$1 \times 7 = 7$   $10 \times 7 = 70$   $7 \times 7 = 49$   $6 \times 7 = 42$   $7 \times 5 = 35$

$0 \times 7 = 0$   $7 \times 4 = 28$   $11 \times 7 = 77$

**B**

$(3 \times 7) + 6 =$   $(2 \times 7) + 5 =$   $(4 \times 7) + 3 =$   $(5 \times 7) + 4 =$

$(9 \times 7) + 2 =$   $(7 \times 7) + 5 =$   $(6 \times 7) + 2 =$   $(8 \times 7) + 5 =$

$(3 \times 7) + 3 =$   $(6 \times 7) + 3 =$   $(8 \times 7) + 4 =$   $(2 \times 7) + 6 =$

$(4 \times 7) + 5 =$   $(7 \times 7) + 4 =$   $(5 \times 7) + 2 =$   $(9 \times 7) + 6 =$

$(3 \times 7) + 4 =$   $(8 \times 7) + 6 =$   $(9 \times 7) + 4 =$   $(4 \times 7) + 6 =$

$(2 \times 7) + 2 =$   $(5 \times 7) + 3 =$   $(7 \times 7) + 3 =$

**C**

| 426 | 396 | 457 | 187 | 609 | 148 |
| $\times 7$ | $\times 7$ | $\times 7$ | $\times 7$ | $\times 7$ | $\times 7$ |

| 324 | 635 | 298 | 439 | 177 | 208 |
| $\times 7$ | $\times 7$ | $\times 7$ | $\times 7$ | $\times 7$ | $\times 7$ |

| 1235 | 1389 | 1176 | 1068 | 1403 |
| $\times 7$ | $\times 7$ | $\times 7$ | $\times 7$ | $\times 7$ |

**D**

$473 \times 7$   $629 \times 7$   $808 \times 7$   $929 \times 7$

$1143 \times 7$   $1086 \times 7$   $1205 \times 7$   $1097 \times 7$

**E**

Find the product of 497 and 7.

Multiply five hundred and nine by seven.

What number is seven times eighty-seven?

Find the product of 379 and 7.

What number is seven times ninety-six?

Multiply three hundred and ten by seven.

# Multiplication by 8

**A**  ☐ × 8 = 16   ☐ × 8 = 64   ☐ × 8 = 24   ☐ × 8 = 48   ☐ × 8 = 96

☐ × 8 = 0   8 × ☐ = 32   ☐ × 8 = 56   ☐ × 8 = 40   ☐ × 8 = 88

☐ × 1 = 8   8 × ☐ = 24   8 × ☐ = 48   ☐ × 8 = 32   ☐ × 8 = 80

8 × ☐ = 16   ☐ × 8 = 72   8 × ☐ = 8   8 × ☐ = 56   8 × ☐ = 40

**B**  Add

64 + 6 = ☐    48 + 2 = ☐    16 + 7 = ☐    24 + 6 = ☐    8 + 2 = ☐

56 + 7 = ☐    48 + 3 = ☐    8 + 4 = ☐    56 + 6 = ☐    64 + 7 = ☐

48 + 5 = ☐    8 + 6 = ☐    56 + 4 = ☐    24 + 7 = ☐    48 + 4 = ☐

16 + 5 = ☐    8 + 7 = ☐    16 + 6 = ☐    48 + 6 = ☐    8 + 5 = ☐

16 + 4 = ☐    48 + 7 = ☐    56 + 5 = ☐    8 + 3 = ☐

**C**

| 327 | 409 | 618 | 520 | 987 | 431 |
|---|---|---|---|---|---|
| ×8 | ×8 | ×8 | ×8 | ×8 | ×8 |

| 606 | 897 | 532 | 170 | 547 | 823 |
|---|---|---|---|---|---|
| ×8 | ×8 | ×8 | ×8 | ×8 | ×8 |

| 1098 | 1209 | 1070 | 1165 | 1143 |
|---|---|---|---|---|
| ×8 | ×8 | ×8 | ×8 | ×8 |

**D**  380 × 8      675 × 8      989 × 8      206 × 8

1149 × 8     1069 × 8     1006 × 8     1124 × 8

**E**  Find the product of   397 and 8   1027 and 8   729 and 8

Multiply by eight

439      1025      929      630      836      1009      606

# Multiplication by 9

**A**

$1 \times 9 = \square$   $9 \times 4 = \square$   $6 \times 9 = \square$   $7 \times 9 = \square$   $0 \times 9 = \square$

$9 \times 5 = \square$   $9 \times 8 = \square$   $4 \times 9 = \square$   $12 \times 9 = \square$   $9 \times 9 = \square$

$9 \times 7 = \square$   $3 \times 9 = \square$   $11 \times 9 = \square$   $2 \times 9 = \square$   $9 \times 2 = \square$

$9 \times 0 = \square$   $5 \times 9 = \square$   $8 \times 9 = \square$   $10 \times 9 = \square$   $9 \times 3 = \square$

$9 \times 6 = \square$

**B**   Add

$9 + 2 = \square$   $36 + 7 = \square$   $36 + 6 = \square$   $27 + 4 = \square$   $31 + 9 = \square$

$9 + 6 = \square$   $63 + 8 = \square$   $63 + 7 = \square$   $27 + 8 = \square$   $72 + 9 = \square$

$27 + 9 = \square$   $18 + 7 = \square$   $27 + 6 = \square$   $9 + 3 = \square$   $54 + 7 = \square$

$36 + 8 = \square$   $27 + 7 = \square$   $45 + 9 = \square$   $72 + 8 = \square$   $27 + 5 = \square$

$9 + 5 = \square$   $18 + 6 = \square$   $9 + 9 = \square$   $18 + 5 = \square$   $36 + 5 = \square$

$45 + 5 = \square$   $63 + 9 = \square$   $18 + 4 = \square$   $9 + 8 = \square$   $45 + 6 = \square$

$45 + 8 = \square$   $54 + 8 = \square$   $18 + 9 = \square$   $54 + 6 = \square$   $54 + 9 = \square$

$18 + 8 = \square$   $9 + 7 = \square$   $36 + 4 = \square$   $18 + 2 = \square$   $45 + 7 = \square$

$27 + 3 = \square$   $9 + 4 = \square$   $36 + 9 = \square$   $9 + 1 = \square$   $18 + 3 = \square$

**C**

| | | | | | |
|---|---|---|---|---|---|
| 427 | 683 | 939 | 157 | 708 | 526 |
| ×9 | ×9 | ×9 | ×9 | ×9 | ×9 |

| | | | | | |
|---|---|---|---|---|---|
| 631 | 760 | 909 | 386 | 825 | 431 |
| ×9 | ×9 | ×9 | ×9 | ×9 | ×9 |

| | | | |
|---|---|---|---|
| 1076 | 1107 | 1035 | 1108 |
| ×9 | ×9 | ×9 | ×9 |

**D**   Copy and fill in the missing numbers.

$$4\,\square \qquad 8\,\square\,9 \qquad 2\;\;5\;\;3 \qquad 1\,\square\,4\,\square$$
$$\underline{\times 9} \qquad \underline{\quad\times 9} \qquad \underline{\quad\;\;\times 9} \qquad \underline{\qquad\times 9}$$
$$\square\,1\;\,4 \qquad 7\;\,2\;\,8\;\,1 \qquad 2\,\square\,7\,\square \qquad \square\,4\;\,0\;\,5$$

# Multiplication by 11

**A**

$7 \times 11 = \boxed{77}$  $4 \times 11 = \boxed{44}$  $3 \times 11 = \boxed{33}$  $1 \times 11 = \boxed{11}$  $9 \times 11 = \boxed{99}$

$8 \times 11 = \boxed{88}$  $2 \times 11 = \boxed{22}$  $6 \times 11 = \boxed{66}$  $5 \times 11 = \boxed{55}$  $0 \times 11 = \boxed{0}$

$11 \times \boxed{8} = 88$  $11 \times \boxed{4} = 44$  $11 \times \boxed{5} = 55$  $11 \times \boxed{1} = 11$  $11 \times \boxed{6} = 66$

$11 \times \boxed{3} = 33$  $11 \times \boxed{7} = 77$  $11 \times \boxed{0} = 0$  $11 \times \boxed{9} = 99$  $11 \times \boxed{2} = 22$

**B**

| | | | | |
|---|---|---|---|---|
| $77 + 4 = \square$ | $88 + 8 = \square$ | $44 + 7 = \square$ | $77 + 5 = \square$ | $66 + 6 = \square$ |
| $77 + 3 = \square$ | $33 + 9 = \square$ | $77 + 6 = \square$ | $88 + 9 = \square$ | $55 + 9 = \square$ |
| $66 + 7 = \square$ | $88 + 6 = \square$ | $77 + 7 = \square$ | $55 + 6 = \square$ | $99 + 9 = \square$ |
| $88 + 7 = \square$ | $99 + 8 = \square$ | $33 + 7 = \square$ | $66 + 9 = \square$ | $22 + 9 = \square$ |
| $55 + 5 = \square$ | $22 + 8 = \square$ | $77 + 9 = \square$ | $66 + 8 = \square$ | $55 + 7 = \square$ |
| $99 + 7 = \square$ | $55 + 8 = \square$ | $66 + 5 = \square$ | $99 + 5 = \square$ | $88 + 3 = \square$ |
| $33 + 8 = \square$ | $77 + 8 = \square$ | $44 + 9 = \square$ | $99 + 6 = \square$ | $44 + 8 = \square$ |
| $99 + 2 = \square$ | $88 + 4 = \square$ | $99 + 3 = \square$ | $88 + 5 = \square$ | $88 + 2 = \square$ |
| $99 + 1 = \square$ | $11 + 9 = \square$ | $66 + 4 = \square$ | $44 + 6 = \square$ | $99 + 4 = \square$ |

**C**

| | | | | | |
|---|---|---|---|---|---|
| 235 | 404 | 678 | 172 | 287 | 356 |
| ×11 | ×11 | ×11 | ×11 | ×11 | ×11 |

| | | | | | |
|---|---|---|---|---|---|
| 140 | 906 | 825 | 732 | 624 | 382 |
| ×11 | ×11 | ×11 | ×11 | ×11 | ×11 |

**D**  Multiply by eleven

three hundred and sixty-seven

five hundred and seven

one hundred and forty

# Multiplication by 12

**A**  $4 \times 12 = \square$   $9 \times 12 = \square$   $5 \times 12 = \square$   $3 \times 12 = \square$   $1 \times 12 = \square$

  $0 \times 12 = \square$   $2 \times 12 = \square$   $8 \times 12 = \square$   $7 \times 12 = \square$   $6 \times 12 = \square$

  $12 \times \square = 12$   $12 \times \square = 60$   $12 \times \square = 84$   $12 \times \square = 36$   $12 \times \square = 108$

  $12 \times \square = 48$   $12 \times \square = 72$   $12 \times \square = 24$   $12 \times \square = 0$   $12 \times \square = 96$

**B**  $36 \div 5 = \square$   $12 \div 9 = \square$   $108 \div 3 = \square$   $72 \div 8 = \square$   $36 \div 6 = \square$

  $108 \div 4 = \square$   $84 \div 8 = \square$   $24 \div 7 = \square$   $108 \div 2 = \square$   $48 \div 5 = \square$

  $96 \div 4 = \square$   $48 \div 3 = \square$   $24 \div 6 = \square$   $48 \div 2 = \square$   $96 \div 6 = \square$

  $96 \div 5 = \square$   $48 \div 4 = \square$   $24 \div 8 = \square$   $96 \div 8 = \square$   $48 \div 7 = \square$

  $108 \div 8 = \square$   $12 \div 8 = \square$   $108 \div 7 = \square$   $72 \div 9 = \square$   $36 \div 4 = \square$

  $84 \div 9 = \square$   $48 \div 8 = \square$   $36 \div 8 = \square$   $24 \div 9 = \square$   $108 \div 6 = \square$

  $108 \div 9 = \square$   $96 \div 9 = \square$   $84 \div 6 = \square$   $48 \div 6 = \square$   $96 \div 7 = \square$

  $36 \div 9 = \square$   $48 \div 9 = \square$   $84 \div 7 = \square$   $108 \div 5 = \square$   $36 \div 7 = \square$

**C**

| 726 | 450 | 375 | 165 | 270 | 802 |
|---|---|---|---|---|---|
| ×12 | ×12 | ×12 | ×12 | ×12 | ×12 |

**D**  479 × 12     729 × 12         285 × 12         651 × 12

  163 × 12     455 × 12         400 × 12         394 × 12

  821 × 12     666 × 12

**E**  Find the product of   430 and 12

         636 and 12

         521 and 12

  Multiply by 12         386     346     409     814     707

# Multiplication — miscellaneous

**A**

| 47 | 56 | 89 | 32 | 91 | 70 | 68 |
|---|---|---|---|---|---|---|
| ×5 | ×7 | ×4 | ×3 | ×5 | ×6 | ×2 |

| 95 | 43 | 55 | 80 | 39 | 67 | 75 |
|---|---|---|---|---|---|---|
| ×7 | ×9 | ×8 | ×12 | ×9 | ×11 | ×8 |

| 172 | 698 | 534 | 901 | 508 | 476 |
|---|---|---|---|---|---|
| ×8 | ×3 | ×11 | ×2 | ×12 | ×6 |

| 202 | 572 | 398 | 641 | 920 | 731 |
|---|---|---|---|---|---|
| ×4 | ×9 | ×7 | ×7 | ×6 | ×5 |

| 4127 | 3048 | 1472 | 1731 | 1079 |
|---|---|---|---|---|
| ×2 | ×3 | ×5 | ×4 | ×7 |

| 1168 | 1034 | 1006 | 3541 | 2345 |
|---|---|---|---|---|
| ×8 | ×9 | ×7 | ×2 | ×3 |

**B** Solve by multiplication

58 + 58 + 58 + 58 + 58 + 58 + 58 + 58

427 + 427 + 427 + 427

1027 + 1027 + 1027 + 1027

698 + 698 + 698 + 698 + 698

**C** Find the product of

355 and 9          1076 and 8

463 and 12         2047 and 4

**D** Multiply three thousand and six by three.

What number is six times ninety-seven?

What number is four times three hundred and ten?

Find the product of          1247 and 4          1309 and 6          1099 and 8

Multiply one thousand and twelve by seven.

# Division — revision

**A**

| | | | | | |
|---|---|---|---|---|---|
| 2 $\overline{)666}$ | 3 $\overline{)999}$ | 4 $\overline{)888}$ | 6 $\overline{)666}$ | 5 $\overline{)555}$ | 2 $\overline{)444}$ |
| 2 $\overline{)184}$ | 3 $\overline{)153}$ | 4 $\overline{)244}$ | 5 $\overline{)255}$ | 6 $\overline{)186}$ | 5 $\overline{)355}$ |
| 3 $\overline{)516}$ | 4 $\overline{)768}$ | 5 $\overline{)755}$ | 6 $\overline{)966}$ | 4 $\overline{)644}$ | 3 $\overline{)543}$ |
| 3 $\overline{)575}$ | 4 $\overline{)726}$ | 5 $\overline{)957}$ | 6 $\overline{)849}$ | 6 $\overline{)788}$ | 5 $\overline{)657}$ |
| 4 $\overline{)852}$ | 5 $\overline{)595}$ | 4 $\overline{)476}$ | 6 $\overline{)684}$ | 3 $\overline{)981}$ | 2 $\overline{)478}$ |
| 3 $\overline{)861}$ | 6 $\overline{)972}$ | 5 $\overline{)780}$ | 2 $\overline{)972}$ | 6 $\overline{)864}$ | 4 $\overline{)776}$ |
| 5 $\overline{)540}$ | 4 $\overline{)836}$ | 5 $\overline{)545}$ | 3 $\overline{)927}$ | 6 $\overline{)654}$ | 2 $\overline{)818}$ |
| 6 $\overline{)675}$ | 2 $\overline{)579}$ | 5 $\overline{)748}$ | 3 $\overline{)763}$ | 4 $\overline{)975}$ | 3 $\overline{)826}$ |
| 2 $\overline{)340}$ | 5 $\overline{)750}$ | 6 $\overline{)840}$ | 4 $\overline{)760}$ | 6 $\overline{)960}$ | 5 $\overline{)650}$ |
| 2 $\overline{)660}$ | 4 $\overline{)840}$ | 3 $\overline{)690}$ | 5 $\overline{)550}$ | 3 $\overline{)390}$ | 2 $\overline{)820}$ |
| 3 $\overline{)600}$ | 4 $\overline{)800}$ | 2 $\overline{)400}$ | 3 $\overline{)900}$ | 3 $\overline{)600}$ | 2 $\overline{)800}$ |
| 4 $\overline{)707}$ | 5 $\overline{)708}$ | 3 $\overline{)704}$ | 6 $\overline{)904}$ | 6 $\overline{)805}$ | 5 $\overline{)807}$ |
| 4 $\overline{)790}$ | 5 $\overline{)473}$ | 3 $\overline{)502}$ | 2 $\overline{)670}$ | 6 $\overline{)529}$ | 4 $\overline{)902}$ |

**B**

476 ÷ 5          396 ÷ 6          854 ÷ 4

839 ÷ 2          765 ÷ 3          929 ÷ 4

**C**

Divide 470 by 4.                    Share 973 by 3.

How many 5s in 543?           How many 2s in 763?

Share 867 by 6.                     Divide 374 by 4.

# Division — thousands

**A**

| | | | | |
|---|---|---|---|---|
| 2)6842 | 4)8448 | 3)6939 | 2)8246 | 3)3963 |
| 3)1254 | 6)1866 | 2)1284 | 5)1555 | 4)1684 |
| 4)3649 | 5)4556 | 3)2168 | 2)1664 | 6)3667 |
| 6)7868 | 4)6848 | 5)8556 | 2)7886 | 3)8167 |
| 5)8657 | 2)7563 | 3)8258 | 6)7569 | 4)9567 |
| 2)3573 | 6)1572 | 3)5264 | 5)7845 | 4)6693 |
| 5)5473 | 2)2176 | 4)4372 | 3)9251 | 6)6583 |
| 6)9645 | 4)7632 | 3)7521 | 2)1812 | 5)6538 |
| 4)6563 | 2)9761 | 6)8823 | 3)5852 | 5)7854 |
| 6)5822 | 2)1818 | 3)6244 | 4)8273 | 5)4543 |
| 2)8035 | 4)7205 | 3)9048 | 6)8406 | 5)3505 |
| 2)4015 | 5)5025 | 3)6027 | 6)6054 | 4)8034 |

**B**  Divide 1247 by 2.              Share 7603 by 6.
    Divide 5037 by 5.              Share 8321 by 4.

**C**  How many threes in three thousand and six?
    How many times can six be taken from four thousand and eighty-nine?
    Share six thousand into four equal parts.

# Division by 7

**A**
| | | | | |
|---|---|---|---|---|
| 14 ÷ 7 = ☐ | 49 ÷ 7 = ☐ | 21 ÷ 7 = ☐ | 63 ÷ 7 = ☐ | 0 ÷ 7 = ☐ |
| 35 ÷ 7 = ☐ | 56 ÷ 7 = ☐ | 7 ÷ 7 = ☐ | 28 ÷ 7 = ☐ | 42 ÷ 7 = ☐ |

**B**
| | | | | |
|---|---|---|---|---|
| 62 − 56 = ☐ | 41 − 35 = ☐ | 20 − 14 = ☐ | 54 − 49 = ☐ | 33 − 28 = ☐ |
| 13 − 7 = ☐ | 60 − 56 = ☐ | 52 − 49 = ☐ | 30 − 28 = ☐ | 55 − 49 = ☐ |
| 32 − 28 = ☐ | 61 − 56 = ☐ | 50 − 49 = ☐ | 12 − 7 = ☐ | 40 − 35 = ☐ |
| 53 − 49 = ☐ | 11 − 7 = ☐ | 51 − 49 = ☐ | 34 − 28 = ☐ | 31 − 28 = ☐ |

**C**

| | | | | |
|---|---|---|---|---|
| 7⟌55 | 7⟌53 | 7⟌12 | 7⟌61 | 7⟌32 |
| 7⟌52 | 7⟌30 | 7⟌62 | 7⟌20 | 7⟌33 |
| 7⟌11 | 7⟌60 | 7⟌51 | 7⟌13 | 7⟌40 |
| 7⟌54 | 7⟌34 | 7⟌50 | 7⟌41 | 7⟌31 |

**D**

| | | | | | | |
|---|---|---|---|---|---|---|
| 7⟌95 | 7⟌87 | 7⟌79 | 7⟌83 | 7⟌92 | 7⟌78 | 7⟌89 |

| | | | | | |
|---|---|---|---|---|---|
| 7⟌135 | 7⟌146 | 7⟌164 | 7⟌151 | 7⟌182 | 7⟌173 |

| | | | | | |
|---|---|---|---|---|---|
| 7⟌943 | 7⟌408 | 7⟌567 | 7⟌680 | 7⟌874 | 7⟌362 |

| | | | | |
|---|---|---|---|---|
| 7⟌1543 | 7⟌1739 | 7⟌1962 | 7⟌1808 | 7⟌1650 |

| | | | | |
|---|---|---|---|---|
| 7⟌6306 | 7⟌3435 | 7⟌4389 | 7⟌5928 | 7⟌2769 |

| | | | | |
|---|---|---|---|---|
| 7⟌8607 | 7⟌7350 | 7⟌8846 | 7⟌9429 | 7⟌9707 |

**E** Divide by seven

| | | | | |
|---|---|---|---|---|
| 4271 | 909 | 4210 | 1435 | 892 |

# Division by 8

**A**

$8\overline{)24}$        $8\overline{)72}$        $8\overline{)\,0}$        $8\overline{)64}$        $8\overline{)16}$

$8\overline{)48}$        $8\overline{)\,8}$        $8\overline{)56}$        $8\overline{)32}$        $8\overline{)40}$

**B**

| | | | | |
|---|---|---|---|---|
| 63 − 56 = ☐ | 23 − 16 = ☐ | 54 − 48 = ☐ | 71 − 64 = ☐ | 31 − 24 = ☐ |
| 15 − 8 = ☐ | 61 − 56 = ☐ | 21 − 16 = ☐ | 11 − 8 = ☐ | 55 − 48 = ☐ |
| 70 − 64 = ☐ | 51 − 48 = ☐ | 13 − 8 = ☐ | 62 − 56 = ☐ | 53 − 48 = ☐ |
| 14 − 8 = ☐ | 60 − 56 = ☐ | 30 − 24 = ☐ | 12 − 8 = ☐ | 20 − 16 = ☐ |
| 10 − 8 = ☐ | 52 − 48 = ☐ | 22 − 16 = ☐ | 50 − 48 = ☐ | |

**C**

| | | | | | |
|---|---|---|---|---|---|
| 15 ÷ 8 | 63 ÷ 8 | 52 ÷ 8 | 20 ÷ 8 | 71 ÷ 8 | 30 ÷ 8 |
| 12 ÷ 8 | 54 ÷ 8 | 60 ÷ 8 | 11 ÷ 8 | 53 ÷ 8 | 70 ÷ 8 |
| 23 ÷ 8 | 10 ÷ 8 | 55 ÷ 8 | 62 ÷ 8 | 22 ÷ 8 | 50 ÷ 8 |
| 51 ÷ 8 | 14 ÷ 8 | 61 ÷ 8 | 21 ÷ 8 | 13 ÷ 8 | 31 ÷ 8 |

**D**

$8\overline{)95}$    $8\overline{)87}$    $8\overline{)96}$    $8\overline{)88}$    $8\overline{)93}$    $8\overline{)98}$    $8\overline{)89}$

$8\overline{)147}$    $8\overline{)186}$    $8\overline{)192}$    $8\overline{)142}$    $8\overline{)106}$    $8\overline{)155}$

$8\overline{)946}$    $8\overline{)972}$    $8\overline{)806}$    $8\overline{)909}$    $8\overline{)992}$    $8\overline{)958}$

$8\overline{)1962}$    $8\overline{)1179}$    $8\overline{)1894}$    $8\overline{)1758}$    $8\overline{)1632}$

$8\overline{)7506}$    $8\overline{)6330}$    $8\overline{)5749}$    $8\overline{)7072}$    $8\overline{)4752}$

$8\overline{)8903}$    $8\overline{)9243}$    $8\overline{)9071}$    $8\overline{)8749}$    $8\overline{)9673}$

**E**    4320 ÷ 8        9041 ÷ 8        729 ÷ 8        1690 ÷ 8

# Division by 9

**A**

$\square \div 9 = 6$    $\square \div 9 = 9$    $\square \div 9 = 2$    $\square \div 9 = 4$    $\square \div 9 = 7$

$\square \div 9 = 0$    $\square \div 9 = 5$    $\square \div 9 = 1$    $\square \div 9 = 3$    $\square \div 9 = 8$

**B**

| | | | | | | |
|---|---|---|---|---|---|---|
| 9)70 | 9)26 | 9)53 | 9)33 | 9)23 | 9)42 | 9)20 |
| 9)30 | 9)12 | 9)62 | 9)43 | 9)80 | 9)50 | 9)60 |
| 9)13 | 9)34 | 9)21 | 9)11 | 9)32 | 9)22 | 9)16 |
| 9)52 | 9)61 | 9)51 | 9)24 | 9)71 | 9)41 | 9)40 |
| 9)14 | 9)25 | 9)44 | 9)35 | 9)15 | 9)17 | 9)31 |

**C**

| | | | | | |
|---|---|---|---|---|---|
| 9)106 | 9)123 | 9)144 | 9)192 | 9)137 | 9)187 |
| 9)175 | 9)146 | 9)181 | 9)110 | 9)199 | 9)168 |
| 9)619 | 9)820 | 9)332 | 9)264 | 9)676 | 9)488 |
| 9)563 | 9)401 | 9)529 | 9)255 | 9)767 | 9)309 |

| | | | | |
|---|---|---|---|---|
| 9)1301 | 9)1274 | 9)1165 | 9)1750 | 9)1639 |
| 9)8193 | 9)1083 | 9)1416 | 9)7657 | 9)1848 |
| 9)6039 | 9)2300 | 9)3945 | 9)5466 | 9)6578 |

**D**   Share by nine

| | | | |
|---|---|---|---|
| 376 | 4207 | 3943 | 680 |
| 5279 | 809 | 976 | 8280 |

How many groups of nine in

476?     2146?     1906?     694?     923?

# Division by 11

**A**  33 ÷ 11 = ☐   66 ÷ 11 = ☐   88 ÷ 11 = ☐   11 ÷ 11 = ☐   99 ÷ 11 = ☐
   77 ÷ 11 = ☐   55 ÷ 11 = ☐   0 ÷ 11 = ☐   44 ÷ 11 = ☐   22 ÷ 11 = ☐

**B**  20 − 11 = ☐   97 − 88 = ☐   84 − 77 = ☐   52 − 44 = ☐   42 − 33 = ☐
   81 − 77 = ☐   73 − 66 = ☐   41 − 33 = ☐   94 − 88 = ☐   64 − 55 = ☐
   96 − 88 = ☐   62 − 55 = ☐   30 − 22 = ☐   75 − 66 = ☐   40 − 33 = ☐
   71 − 66 = ☐   53 − 44 = ☐   92 − 88 = ☐   63 − 55 = ☐   51 − 44 = ☐
   93 − 88 = ☐   86 − 77 = ☐   72 − 66 = ☐   50 − 44 = ☐   95 − 88 = ☐
   80 − 77 = ☐   91 − 88 = ☐   70 − 66 = ☐   31 − 22 = ☐   83 − 77 = ☐
   61 − 55 = ☐   82 − 77 = ☐   60 − 55 = ☐   85 − 77 = ☐   74 − 66 = ☐

**C**

11 | 150      11 | 141      11 | 173      11 | 192      11 | 165      11 | 186

11 | 674      11 | 590      11 | 869      11 | 482      11 | 334      11 | 752

11 | 103      11 | 105      11 | 109      11 | 108      11 | 107      11 | 106

11 | 1607     11 | 1983     11 | 1736     11 | 1870     11 | 1525

11 | 7249     11 | 2207     11 | 8125     11 | 9936     11 | 4510

11 | 1074     11 | 1029     11 | 1030     11 | 1056     11 | 1063

**D**  How many groups of eleven in

   3432?              605?              5841?              352?
   6270?              9174?              308?              902?

Divide by 11

6294              942              2201              814              1098

# Division by 12

**A**

$12\overline{)108}$    $12\overline{)24}$    $12\overline{)36}$    $12\overline{)72}$    $12\overline{)12}$

$12\overline{)60}$    $12\overline{)84}$    $12\overline{)96}$    $12\overline{)0}$    $12\overline{)48}$

**B**

$12\overline{)43}$    $12\overline{)56}$    $12\overline{)33}$    $12\overline{)104}$    $12\overline{)81}$    $12\overline{)101}$

$12\overline{)90}$    $12\overline{)42}$    $12\overline{)82}$    $12\overline{)102}$    $12\overline{)52}$    $12\overline{)105}$

$12\overline{)20}$    $12\overline{)91}$    $12\overline{)51}$    $12\overline{)100}$    $12\overline{)81}$    $12\overline{)103}$

$12\overline{)55}$    $12\overline{)41}$    $12\overline{)21}$    $12\overline{)50}$    $12\overline{)57}$    $12\overline{)58}$

$12\overline{)93}$    $12\overline{)94}$    $12\overline{)53}$    $12\overline{)46}$    $12\overline{)92}$    $12\overline{)30}$

$12\overline{)32}$    $12\overline{)45}$    $12\overline{)54}$    $12\overline{)40}$    $12\overline{)80}$    $12\overline{)44}$

**C**

$12\overline{)749}$    $12\overline{)684}$    $12\overline{)379}$    $12\overline{)364}$    $12\overline{)851}$    $12\overline{)929}$

$12\overline{)478}$    $12\overline{)607}$    $12\overline{)963}$    $12\overline{)729}$    $12\overline{)216}$    $12\overline{)414}$

$12\overline{)113}$    $12\overline{)111}$    $12\overline{)112}$    $12\overline{)117}$    $12\overline{)110}$    $12\overline{)115}$

$12\overline{)2046}$    $12\overline{)2301}$    $12\overline{)2192}$    $12\overline{)2210}$    $12\overline{)1937}$

$12\overline{)9704}$    $12\overline{)7530}$    $12\overline{)6760}$    $12\overline{)2921}$    $12\overline{)4785}$

$12\overline{)1165}$    $12\overline{)1024}$    $12\overline{)1072}$    $12\overline{)1193}$    $12\overline{)1150}$

**D**

| | | |
|---|---|---|
| $7216 \div 12$ | $3406 \div 12$ | $808 \div 12$ |
| $7206 \div 12$ | $4200 \div 12$ | $8833 \div 12$ |
| $1111 \div 12$ | $404 \div 12$ | |

**E**    How many groups of twelve in

2076?    986?    4270?    6735?    406?

# Notation

**A** Write in words the value of the 7 in these numbers.

7463      2765      2617      5670      2007

4799      8673      7421      3740      7621

**B** Rearrange each group of figures to make the largest number possible.

4516      8103      4973      9624      1003

1077      9427      1083      3562      7462

**C** Multiply each number by 10 and write its value in words.

362      75      9      81      427      808

Multiply each number by 100 and write its value in words.

5      46      50      8      96      72

7      12

**D** Divide each number by 10 and write its value in words.

370      40      4270      6320      580      70

Divide each number by 100 and write its value in words.

3400      300      7100      800      5200

**E** Write what you must do to make

7 become 70.      340 become 34.

4000 become 40.      50 become 500.

20 become 2000.      60 become 6.

**F** Find the value of X in the following.

$550 = X \times 10$      $4500 = X \times 10$      $1300 = X \times 100$

$1020 = X \times 10$      $630 = X \times 10$      $1450 = X \times 10$

$41 = X \div 100$      $6 = X \div 100$      $92 = X \div 10$

$320 = X \div 10$      $104 = X \div 10$      $16 = X \div 100$

# Number series and equations

**A** Write out and complete the number series.

4, 8, ☐, 16, 20, ☐, 28, ☐          7, 14, 21, 28, ☐, ☐, ☐

9, 12, ☐, ☐, 21, 24, ☐          48, ☐, 72, 84, 96, ☐, ☐

81, 72, 63, ☐, ☐, 36, ☐          88, 80, 72, ☐, ☐, ☐

50, ☐, 70, ☐, 90, ☐          ☐, 14, 16, ☐, 20, 22, ☐

24, 22, 20, ☐, ☐, ☐          ☐, 90, ☐, 70, ☐, 50, ☐

☐, 10, 15, ☐, ☐, ☐, 35          32, ☐, 24, ☐, 16, 12, ☐

66, ☐, 44, 33, ☐, ☐          55, 66, 77, ☐, ☐, ☐

24, 32, ☐, ☐, 56, 64, ☐          ☐, 27, 36, ☐, ☐, 63, 72

48, 42, ☐, 30, ☐, 18, ☐          77, ☐, 63, ☐, 49, ☐, 35

**B** Write out and complete these number series.

3, 6, 10, 13, 17, ☐, ☒, ☐, ☒

52, 47, 39, 34, 26, ☐, ☐, ☒, ☐

2, 8, 10, 16, 18, ☐, ☐, ☐, ☐

62, 61, 55, 54, 48, ☐, ☐, ☐, ☐

4, 11, 19, 26, 34, ☐, ☐, ☐, ☐

24, 22, 19, 17, 14, ☐, ☐, ☐, ☐

8, 13, 22, 27, 36, ☐, ☐, ☐, ☐

54, 50, 43, 39, 32, ☐, ☐, ☐, ☐

**C** Write and complete the equations.

$6 \times 2 = \boxed{\phantom{0}} \times 4$          $4 \times 3 = \boxed{\phantom{0}} \times 6$          $4 \times 6 = \boxed{\phantom{0}} \times 3$

$\boxed{\phantom{0}} \times 8 = 4 \times 12$          $9 \times 4 = \boxed{\phantom{0}} \times 6$          $2 \times \boxed{\phantom{0}} = 4 \times 6$

$10 \times 4 = 8 \times \boxed{\phantom{0}}$          $6 \times \boxed{\phantom{0}} = 3 \times 8$          $10 \times \boxed{\phantom{0}} = 8 \times 5$

$8 \times \boxed{\phantom{0}} = 12 \times 2$          $8 \times \boxed{\phantom{0}} = 4 \times 12$          $3 \times 4 = \boxed{\phantom{0}} \times 6$

$\boxed{\phantom{0}} \times 9 = 6 \times 6$          $12 \times 4 = \boxed{\phantom{0}} \times 8$          $\boxed{\phantom{0}} \times 12 = 6 \times 2$

$12 \times 5 = \boxed{\phantom{0}} \times 10$          $5 \times 12 = \boxed{\phantom{0}} \times 6$          $10 \times 4 = \boxed{\phantom{0}} \times 8$

$2 \times 10 = 4 \times \boxed{\phantom{0}}$          $3 \times 8 = \boxed{\phantom{0}} \times 12$          $8 \times 6 = \boxed{\phantom{0}} \times 4$

$\boxed{\phantom{0}} \times 8 = 4 \times 4$          $\boxed{\phantom{0}} \times 10 = 8 \times 5$          $12 \times 2 = \boxed{\phantom{0}} \times 6$

$12 \times \boxed{\phantom{0}} = 2 \times 6$          $8 \times 3 = \boxed{\phantom{0}} \times 4$          $5 \times \boxed{\phantom{0}} = 2 \times 10$

# Division

**A**

| | | | | | |
|---|---|---|---|---|---|
| 2⟌93 | 12⟌97 | 4⟌63 | 3⟌85 | 7⟌90 | 10⟌90 |

| | | | | | |
|---|---|---|---|---|---|
| 12⟌89 | 8⟌75 | 6⟌49 | 11⟌98 | 5⟌39 | 9⟌71 |

| | | | | | |
|---|---|---|---|---|---|
| 2⟌730 | 3⟌745 | 7⟌962 | 6⟌854 | 4⟌918 | 5⟌870 |

| | | | | | |
|---|---|---|---|---|---|
| 5⟌195 | 7⟌189 | 3⟌163 | 4⟌158 | 2⟌137 | 6⟌176 |

| | | | | | |
|---|---|---|---|---|---|
| 12⟌837 | 7⟌654 | 11⟌439 | 8⟌546 | 9⟌752 | 10⟌639 |

| | | | | |
|---|---|---|---|---|
| 5⟌7472 | 3⟌5914 | 2⟌5345 | 4⟌7654 | 6⟌8254 |

| | | | | |
|---|---|---|---|---|
| 11⟌1669 | 12⟌1954 | 9⟌1743 | 10⟌1265 | 8⟌1943 |

| | | | | |
|---|---|---|---|---|
| 7⟌6743 | 5⟌4536 | 8⟌7325 | 6⟌9435 | 4⟌3726 |

| | | | | |
|---|---|---|---|---|
| 4⟌1228 | 5⟌2350 | 7⟌6342 | 8⟌6640 | 12⟌8400 |

| | | | | |
|---|---|---|---|---|
| 4⟌4028 | 5⟌6520 | 8⟌9840 | 9⟌9468 | 3⟌9018 |

**B**  How many twelves make three hundred and forty-eight?

Share two thousand and eight by three.

Divide four thousand and sixty by seven.

How many groups of eight in two thousand?

What must be added to one thousand and fifteen so that it will divide equally by seven?

**C**

| | | | |
|---|---|---|---|
| 4206 ÷ 8 | 379 ÷ 4 | 1463 ÷ 11 | 909 ÷ 5 |
| 8080 ÷ 12 | 600 ÷ 7 | 3607 ÷ 6 | 627 ÷ 9 |

# Fractions — $\frac{1}{2}$ and $\frac{1}{4}$

**A** What fraction of each shape is   **a** shaded?   **b** unshaded?

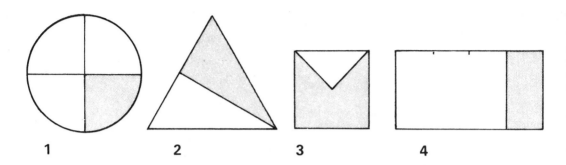

1          2          3          4

**B**

A

B

C

D

Which line is $\frac{1}{2}$ of B?          Which line is $\frac{1}{2}$ of A?

Which line is $\frac{1}{4}$ of A?          Which line is $\frac{3}{4}$ of A?

**C**  How many cm is

$\frac{1}{4}$ of A?          $\frac{1}{2}$ of C?          $\frac{1}{2}$ of B?

$\frac{1}{2}$ of D?          $\frac{1}{4}$ of B?          $\frac{3}{4}$ of A?

**D**  Solve

$\frac{1}{2}$ of 6p          $\frac{1}{4}$ of 8          $\frac{3}{4}$ of 12p          $\frac{1}{2}$ of 20

$\frac{1}{4}$ of 16          $\frac{1}{2}$ of 24p          $\frac{1}{4}$ of 20          $\frac{3}{4}$ of 24

$\frac{1}{2}$ of 40p          $\frac{1}{4}$ of 40          $\frac{3}{4}$ of 40          $\frac{1}{2}$ of 18

**E**  Write and complete

$\frac{3}{4} + \frac{1}{4} = \boxed{\phantom{0}}$          $\frac{1}{4} + \frac{1}{4} = \boxed{\phantom{0}}$          $\frac{1}{2} + \frac{1}{4} = \boxed{\phantom{0}}$          $\frac{1}{4} + \frac{1}{2} + \frac{1}{4} = \boxed{\phantom{0}}$

$1 - \frac{1}{4} = \boxed{\phantom{0}}$          $\frac{3}{4} - \frac{1}{4} = \boxed{\phantom{0}}$          $1 - \frac{1}{2} = \boxed{\phantom{0}}$          $\frac{1}{2} - \frac{1}{4} = \boxed{\phantom{0}}$

$\frac{3}{4} + \frac{3}{4} = \boxed{\phantom{0}}$          $\frac{1}{2} + \frac{3}{4} = \boxed{\phantom{0}}$          $1\frac{1}{4} - \frac{1}{2} = \boxed{\phantom{0}}$          $1\frac{1}{2} - \frac{3}{4} = \boxed{\phantom{0}}$

# Fractions — $\frac{1}{8}$

**A** What fraction of each shape is **a** shaded? **b** unshaded?

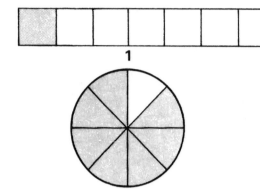

1

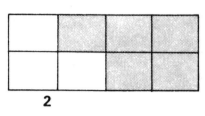

2

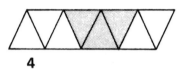

4

3

**B**     $1 = \dfrac{\square}{8}$          $3 = \dfrac{\square}{8}$          $2 = \dfrac{\square}{8}$          $4 = \dfrac{\square}{8}$

**C**     $1\frac{5}{8} = \dfrac{\square}{8}$          $2\frac{3}{8} = \dfrac{\square}{8}$          $1\frac{1}{8} = \dfrac{\square}{8}$          $2\frac{5}{8} = \dfrac{\square}{8}$

**D**     $\dfrac{1}{4} = \dfrac{\square}{8}$          $\dfrac{3}{4} = \dfrac{\square}{8}$          $\dfrac{2}{4} = \dfrac{\square}{8}$          $\dfrac{1}{2} = \dfrac{\square}{8}$

**E**     $1\frac{1}{4} = \dfrac{\square}{8}$          $1\frac{3}{4} = \dfrac{\square}{8}$          $2\frac{1}{2} = \dfrac{\square}{8}$          $1\frac{1}{2} = \dfrac{\square}{8}$

**F**

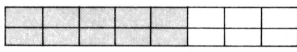

The shape is worth 16.
What is the shaded part worth?
What fraction is shaded?

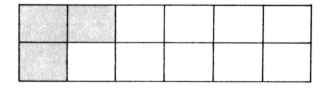

The shape is worth 24.
What is the shaded part worth?
What fraction is shaded?

**G**   Solve

| | | | |
|---|---|---|---|
| $\frac{3}{8}$ of 16 | $\frac{7}{8}$ of 24 | $\frac{1}{4}$ of 16 | $\frac{3}{4}$ of 16 |
| $\frac{3}{4}$ of 24 | $\frac{1}{8}$ of 16 | $\frac{5}{8}$ of 24 | $\frac{1}{8}$ of 24 |
| $\frac{1}{2}$ of 16 | $\frac{1}{4}$ of 24 | $\frac{7}{8}$ of 16 | $\frac{1}{2}$ of 24 |

# Fractions — $\frac{1}{2}$, $\frac{1}{4}$, $\frac{1}{8}$

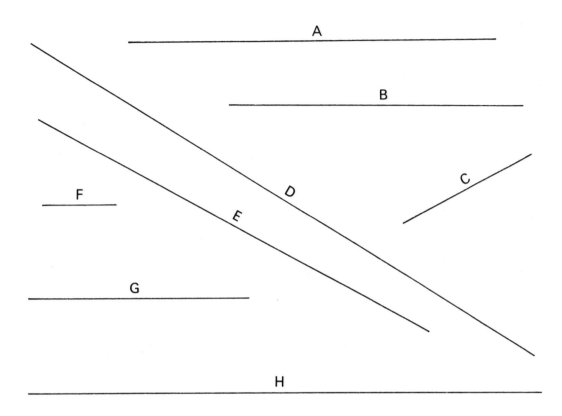

**A**   Which line is

| | | | | |
|---|---|---|---|---|
| $\frac{1}{8}$ of D? | $\frac{1}{4}$ of B? | $\frac{5}{8}$ of D? | $\frac{1}{2}$ of C? | $\frac{3}{4}$ of B? |
| $\frac{1}{2}$ of B? | $\frac{3}{8}$ of D? | $\frac{1}{2}$ of E? | $\frac{7}{8}$ of D? | $\frac{1}{4}$ of D? |

**B**   How many cm is

| | | | |
|---|---|---|---|
| $\frac{5}{8}$ of D? | $\frac{3}{4}$ of E? | $\frac{1}{2}$ of G? | $\frac{1}{8}$ of B? |
| $\frac{1}{4}$ of A? | $\frac{3}{8}$ of B? | $\frac{1}{4}$ of C? | $\frac{3}{4}$ of D? |
| $\frac{1}{2}$ of E? | $\frac{1}{8}$ of D? | $\frac{3}{4}$ of B? | $\frac{1}{4}$ of E? |
| $\frac{7}{8}$ of B? | $\frac{1}{2}$ of H? | $\frac{1}{2}$ of A? | $\frac{1}{2}$ of F? |

**C**   Solve

| | | | |
|---|---|---|---|
| $\frac{3}{8}$ of 64p | $\frac{7}{8}$ of 48 | $\frac{5}{8}$ of 24 g | $\frac{1}{8}$ of 72 |
| $\frac{5}{8}$ of 24 cm | $\frac{1}{2}$ of 23 cm | $\frac{1}{8}$ of 64 cm | $\frac{1}{4}$ of 22 |
| $\frac{3}{4}$ of 48 | $\frac{3}{8}$ of 32p | $\frac{7}{8}$ of 88 | $\frac{5}{8}$ of 96 cm |
| $\frac{1}{8}$ of 56p | $\frac{3}{4}$ of 16 | $\frac{3}{8}$ of 40 g | $\frac{7}{8}$ of 80 g |

# Fractions — $\frac{1}{3}$ and $\frac{1}{6}$

**A**  What fraction of each shape is shaded?

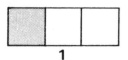

**1**

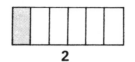

**2**

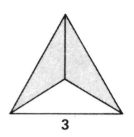

**3**

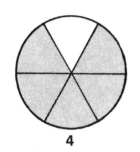

**4**

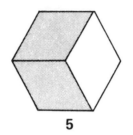

**5**

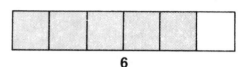

**6**

**B**

| 1 | | |
|---|---|---|
| $\frac{1}{3}$ | $\frac{1}{3}$ | $\frac{1}{3}$ |

| $\frac{1}{6}$ | $\frac{1}{6}$ | $\frac{1}{6}$ | $\frac{1}{6}$ | $\frac{1}{6}$ | $\frac{1}{6}$ |

Complete

$\dfrac{1}{3} = \dfrac{\square}{6}$          $1 = \dfrac{\square}{6}$          $\dfrac{2}{3} = \dfrac{\square}{6}$

$1 = \dfrac{\square}{3}$          $\dfrac{2}{6} = \dfrac{\square}{3}$          $\dfrac{4}{6} = \dfrac{\square}{3}$

$\dfrac{\square}{6} = \dfrac{\square}{3} = 1$

**C**  Write each shaded part in **two** ways.

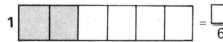

**1**  $= \dfrac{\square}{6} = \dfrac{\square}{3}$

**2**  $= \dfrac{\square}{6} = \dfrac{\square}{3}$

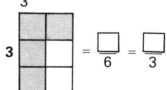

**3**  $= \dfrac{\square}{6} = \dfrac{\square}{3}$

**D**

How many are

$\frac{1}{3}$ of the beads?          $\frac{1}{2}$ of the beads?          $\frac{1}{6}$ of the beads?

$\frac{5}{6}$ of the beads?          $\frac{2}{3}$ of the beads?          $\frac{6}{6}$ of the beads?

# Fractions — $\frac{1}{2}$, $\frac{1}{3}$, $\frac{1}{4}$, $\frac{1}{6}$, $\frac{1}{8}$

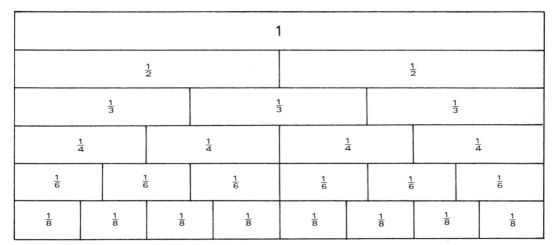

**A**   Copy and complete

$\dfrac{1}{2} = \dfrac{\square}{4}$     $\dfrac{1}{3} = \dfrac{\square}{6}$     $1 = \dfrac{\square}{8}$     $\dfrac{1}{4} = \dfrac{\square}{8}$     $1 = \dfrac{\square}{6}$

$\dfrac{3}{4} = \dfrac{\square}{8}$     $1 = \dfrac{\square}{2}$     $\dfrac{1}{2} = \dfrac{\square}{6}$     $1 = \dfrac{\square}{3}$     $\dfrac{2}{3} = \dfrac{\square}{6}$

$1 = \dfrac{\square}{4}$     $\dfrac{2}{4} = \dfrac{\square}{6}$     $\dfrac{1}{2} = \dfrac{\square}{8}$     $\dfrac{2}{4} = \dfrac{\square}{8}$     $\dfrac{3}{6} = \dfrac{\square}{8}$

**B**

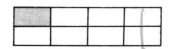

The shape is worth 32.

What fraction is shaded?

What is it worth?

What are the following fractions worth?

$\dfrac{7}{8}$          $\dfrac{1}{4}$          $\dfrac{5}{8}$

$\dfrac{1}{2}$          $\dfrac{3}{8}$

**C**

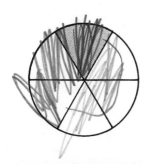

The shaded part is worth 5.

What is the whole shape worth?

What are the following fractions worth?

$\dfrac{1}{2}$          $\dfrac{5}{6}$          $\dfrac{1}{3}$          $\dfrac{2}{3}$

# Fractions — $\frac{1}{5}$ and $\frac{1}{10}$

**A**  What fraction of each shape is   **a** shaded?   **b** unshaded?

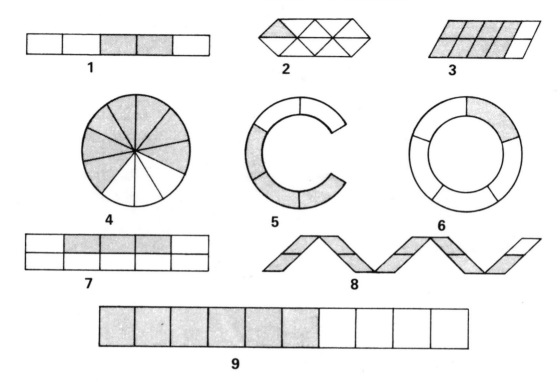

**1**   **2**   **3**

**4**   **5**   **6**

**7**   **8**

**9**

**B**  Complete

$1 = \dfrac{\Box}{10}$        $\dfrac{1}{5} = \dfrac{\Box}{10}$        $\dfrac{4}{10} = \dfrac{\Box}{5}$        $\dfrac{3}{5} = \dfrac{\Box}{10}$        $\dfrac{8}{10} = \dfrac{\Box}{5}$

$\dfrac{6}{10} = \dfrac{\Box}{5}$        $\dfrac{4}{5} = \dfrac{\Box}{10}$        $\dfrac{2}{10} = \dfrac{\Box}{5}$        $1 = \dfrac{\Box}{5}$        $\dfrac{2}{5} = \dfrac{\Box}{10}$

$\dfrac{3}{10} + \dfrac{\Box}{10} = 1$        $\dfrac{2}{5} + \dfrac{\Box}{5} = 1$        $\dfrac{7}{10} + \dfrac{\Box}{10} = 1$        $\dfrac{4}{5} + \dfrac{\Box}{10} = 1$

$\dfrac{1}{5} + \dfrac{\Box}{5} = 1$        $\dfrac{9}{10} + \dfrac{\Box}{10} = 1$        $\dfrac{3}{5} + \dfrac{\Box}{5} = 1$        $\dfrac{1}{10} + \dfrac{\Box}{10} = 1$

**C**  Find the value of

$\frac{1}{5}$ of 25        $\frac{7}{10}$ of 90 cm        $\frac{1}{10}$ of 40 g        $\frac{3}{5}$ of 75

$\frac{3}{10}$ of 60p        $\frac{4}{5}$ of 35        $\frac{9}{10}$ of 20        $\frac{7}{10}$ of 120

$\frac{2}{5}$ of 45 g        $\frac{3}{5}$ of 20p        $\frac{4}{5}$ of 90        $\frac{9}{10}$ of 30

# Fractions

**A**

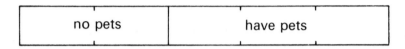

**Class 4**

| brothers | | sisters |

**1** What fraction of the class has a brother?

**2** What fraction of the class has a sister?

**3** What fraction has neither brother nor sister?

**4** There are 30 children in the class.

How many have   **a** a brother?          **b** a sister?          **c** neither?

**B**

| no pets | have pets |

**1** What fraction has pets?

**2** What fraction does not have pets?

**3** There are 16 children with no pet. How many have a pet?

**C**

| saved | spent |

**1** Jill is given 60p each week. What fraction has she saved?

**2** What fraction has she spent?

**3** How much has she   **a** saved?          **b** spent?

**D**

**favourite colours in class 5**

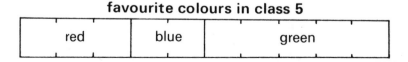

| red | blue | green |

**1** What fraction likes   **a** red?          **b** blue?          **c** green?

**2** There are 40 children in the class. How many children like

**a** red?          **b** blue?          **c** green?

# Decimal notation

**A**  Write as decimals

1  $\frac{2}{10}$        $\frac{5}{10}$        $\frac{7}{10}$        $\frac{3}{10}$        $\frac{6}{10}$

   $\frac{9}{10}$        $\frac{1}{10}$        $\frac{4}{10}$        $\frac{8}{10}$

2  six tenths           four tenths          three tenths

   nine tenths          eight tenths         five tenths

   two tenths           seven tenths

3  $4\frac{7}{10}$        $8\frac{3}{10}$        $2\frac{5}{10}$        $7\frac{9}{10}$        $3\frac{4}{10}$

   $1\frac{6}{10}$        $8\frac{2}{10}$        $5\frac{8}{10}$        $6\frac{1}{10}$

4  eight point five     nine point one       six point two

   three point nine     five point three     seven point four

   nine point eight     four point six       two point seven

5  $\frac{15}{100}$        $\frac{23}{100}$        $\frac{67}{100}$        $\frac{21}{100}$

   $\frac{19}{100}$        $\frac{83}{100}$        $\frac{52}{100}$        $\frac{32}{100}$

6  $\frac{6}{100}$        $\frac{3}{100}$        $\frac{8}{100}$        $\frac{9}{100}$

   $\frac{4}{100}$        $\frac{7}{100}$        $\frac{5}{100}$        $\frac{2}{100}$

   $\frac{1}{100}$

7  $\frac{11}{100}$        $\frac{1}{100}$        $\frac{43}{100}$        $\frac{29}{100}$

   $\frac{7}{100}$        $\frac{3}{100}$        $\frac{9}{100}$        $\frac{2}{100}$

   $\frac{91}{100}$        $\frac{88}{100}$

8  nineteen hundredths          six hundredths

   forty-two hundredths         nine hundredths

9  $4\frac{7}{100}$        $9\frac{15}{100}$        $12\frac{37}{100}$        $8\frac{9}{100}$

   $11\frac{71}{100}$        $4\frac{3}{100}$

10  four units and six hundredths

    nineteen and fifteen hundredths

    five tens, two units and three hundredths

    eight units and sixteen hundredths

**B**  Write the value of the underlined figure in words.

427·63          43·26          19·2          216·02

219·06          32·47          124·23          16·88

127·14          106·27          324·29          43·44

# Decimal notation

**A** Write down the greater of each pair of numbers.

| | | |
|---|---|---|
| 0·4 and 0·37 | 7·02 and 7·1 | 0·99 and 1·01 |
| 4 and 0·47 | 30·2 and 30·06 | 18·23 and 18·7 |
| 0·02 and 0·11 | 14·2 and 14·09 | |

**B** Arrange each line in order of size, beginning with the greatest.

| | | | | | |
|---|---|---|---|---|---|
| 0·11 | 1·01 | 1·10 | 11·05 | 11·10 | 1·11 |
| 1·2 | 1·02 | 1·22 | 2·01 | 1·12 | 1·01 |
| 16·32 | 16·09 | 16·23 | 16·03 | 16·3 | 16·2 |
| 101·09 | 101·9 | 100·99 | 101·99 | 100·09 | 100·9 |

**C** Multiply each number by 10.

| | | | | |
|---|---|---|---|---|
| 42·3 | 42·03 | 76·27 | 85·86 | 143·27 |

**D** Multiply each number by 100.

| | | | | |
|---|---|---|---|---|
| 26·03 | 42·63 | 18·05 | 0·2 | 0·57 |

**E** Divide each number by 10.

| | | | | |
|---|---|---|---|---|
| 24·6 | 91·0 | 303·1 | 42·0 | 271·6 |

**F** Divide each number by 100.

| | | | | |
|---|---|---|---|---|
| 3260 | 421 | 202 | 3400 | 2010 |

**G** Write what you must do to make the 7 worth seven tenths in each number.

| | | | | |
|---|---|---|---|---|
| 37·46 | 73·31 | 62·37 | 70·35 | 7·14 |

**H** Write what you must do to each number to make the 5 worth five units.

| | | | | |
|---|---|---|---|---|
| 0·05 | 53·26 | 7653 | 4521·0 | 62·58 |

# Decimals

**A**  Set down in columns and add.

$4 \cdot 2 + 0 \cdot 02 + 16 \cdot 3$                    $124 \cdot 0 + 3 \cdot 44 + 16.73$

$102 \cdot 3 + 4 \cdot 27 + 3 \cdot 6$                 $12 \cdot 97 + 0 \cdot 09$

$15 \cdot 22 + 101 + 0 \cdot 16$                $4 \cdot 26 + 17 + 92 \cdot 4$

$1 \cdot 2 + 18 \cdot 32 + 216 \cdot 2$             $0 \cdot 07 + 18 \cdot 76 + 4 \cdot 9$


**B**  Set down in columns and subtract.

$18 \cdot 4 - 13 \cdot 26$                       $29 \cdot 2 - 15 \cdot 47$

$27 \cdot 08 - 18 \cdot 3$                       $99 - 0 \cdot 76$

$54 - 3 \cdot 66$                           $42 \cdot 46 - 37 \cdot 09$

$100 - 1 \cdot 07$                         $12 \cdot 04 - 0 \cdot 99$


**C**  Subtract the smaller number from the greater.

$4 \cdot 2$ and $20$                        $12 \cdot 63$ and $14 \cdot 2$

$13 \cdot 6$ and $12 \cdot 99$                  $4.37$ and $18$

$100$ and $94 \cdot 43$                    $18 \cdot 63$ and $7 \cdot 6$

$7 \cdot 2$ and $16 \cdot 33$                 $0 \cdot 98$ and $105 \cdot 2$


**D**  Set down in columns as decimals and add.

$4\frac{1}{10} + 14\frac{7}{100} + 6\frac{11}{100}$          $26\frac{17}{100} + 32\frac{12}{100} + 12\frac{91}{100}$

$8 + 14\frac{13}{100} + \frac{7}{10}$               $13 + 14\frac{1}{10} + 6\frac{92}{100}$

$12\frac{7}{100} + 15 + 26\frac{13}{100}$         $8\frac{3}{10} + 12\frac{7}{10} + 16\frac{31}{100}$

$\frac{18}{100} + 27\frac{3}{10} + 16\frac{2}{10}$          $12\frac{18}{100} + 47 + \frac{83}{100}$


**E**  Set down in columns as decimals and subtract.

$4\frac{3}{10} - 2\frac{17}{100}$                     $100 - \frac{87}{100}$

$18 - 12\frac{18}{100}$                     $9\frac{9}{10} - 8\frac{99}{100}$

$14\frac{17}{100} - 7\frac{5}{10}$                  $26\frac{3}{10} - 18\frac{19}{100}$

$9\frac{1}{10} - 5\frac{36}{100}$                     $42 - 16\frac{7}{100}$


**F**  Fourteen point six minus eight point nine.

Seven point eight four plus nineteen plus six point two.

Find the sum of ninety-six point four and seven point one.

# Money — composition to £1·00

**A** Write down what coins you would receive in change, if you received the least number of coins possible.

| cost | coins given | cost | coins given |
|------|-------------|------|-------------|
| 17p | 1 twenty | 51p | 3 twenties |
| 52p | 1 fifty, 1 ten | 28p | 2 tens, 5 twos |
| 27p | 3 tens | 69p | 7 tens |
| 45p | 2 twenties, 3 twos | 82p | 1 fifty, 2 twenties |
| 21p | 5 fives | 21p | 2 tens, 1 five |
| 62p | 1 fifty, 2 tens | 33p | 3 tens, 2 twos |
| 31p | 4 tens | 22p | 1 ten, 3 fives |
| 41p | 3 tens, 3 fives | 93p | 9 tens, 2 twos |

**B** How much money in each box?

| 50p | 20p | 10p | 5p | 2p | 1p |
|-----|-----|-----|----|----|----|
| 1 | 1 | 2 | 1 | | |

| 50p | 20p | 10p | 5p | 2p | 1p |
|-----|-----|-----|----|----|----|
| 1 | | 2 | 5 | 2 | |

| 50p | 20p | 10p | 5p | 2p | 1p |
|-----|-----|-----|----|----|----|
| | 1 | 3 | 6 | 2 | 3 |

| 50p | 20p | 10p | 5p | 2p | 1p |
|-----|-----|-----|----|----|----|
| | 1 | 3 | 4 | 4 | 2 |

| 50p | 20p | 10p | 5p | 2p | 1p |
|-----|-----|-----|----|----|----|
| 1 | 2 | | | 3 | 2 |

| 50p | 20p | 10p | 5p | 2p | 1p |
|-----|-----|-----|----|----|----|
| | 3 | 2 | | 7 | 3 |

# Money — composition to £1·00

**A**   Find the total of each row of coins.

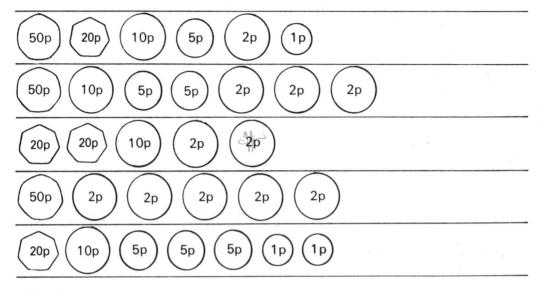

**B**   Which 4 coins make each of these amounts?

| 18p | 15p | 22p | 30p | 16p | 5p | 57p | 75p |

| 8p | 35p | 80p | 64p | 19p | 32p | 12p | 9p |

**C**   Write the coins you would receive in change from 50p after spending each amount, if you received the least number of coins possible.

| 43p | 37p | 29p | 46p | 22p | 28p |

| 33p | 10p | 38p | 27p | 11p | 35p |

**D**   Write the coins you would receive in change from £1·00, after spending each amount, if the least number of coins were given.

76p     42p     35p     67p     24p     14p     87p     93p

**E**   Write **ten** different ways of making 50p with coins.

Write **ten** different ways of making £1·00 with coins.

# Addition and subtraction

**A**

| 27p | 46p | 18p | 34p | 38p | 24p | 46p |
|---|---|---|---|---|---|---|
| +8p | +7p | +26p | +17p | +26p | +58p | +27p |

| 23p | 44p | 32p | 53p | 67p | 76p | 53p |
|---|---|---|---|---|---|---|
| +38p | +26p | +19p | +28p | +27p | +15p | +18p |

| 23p | 24p | 23p | 47p | 36p | 52p | 28p |
|---|---|---|---|---|---|---|
| 42p | 57p | 25p | 8p | 25p | 36p | 42p |
| +16p | +12p | +38p | +32p | +19p | +8p | +11p |

| 26p | 18p | 42p | 42p | 52p | 34p | 27p |
|---|---|---|---|---|---|---|
| 17p | 34p | 23p | 7p | 18p | 22p | 45p |
| +14p | +26p | +18p | +41p | +16p | +33p | +16p |

**B**

| 26p | 35p | 69p | 72p | 88p | 77p | 89p |
|---|---|---|---|---|---|---|
| −4p | −2p | −9p | −1p | −6p | −9p | −5p |

| 35p | 82p | 58p | 82p | 58p | 63p | 78p |
|---|---|---|---|---|---|---|
| −7p | −6p | −7p | −5p | −9p | −5p | −8p |

| 47p | 63p | 71p | 80p | 96p | 32p | 54p |
|---|---|---|---|---|---|---|
| −29p | −22p | −38p | −47p | −55p | −27p | −29p |

| 47p | 63p | 52p | 84p | 96p | 50p | 92p |
|---|---|---|---|---|---|---|
| −28p | −37p | −46p | −53p | −47p | −27p | −34p |

**C**

What is the total of 47p, 20p, 31p?

Find the difference between 52p and 37p.

How much is 62p less than 85p?

Find the sum of 32p, 25p, and 41p.

16p + 27p + 8p + 7p = ☐ p

83p minus 47p

# Multiplication and division

**A**

| | | |
|---|---|---|
| $7p \times 2 = \boxed{\phantom{0}} p$ | $4p \times 6 = \boxed{\phantom{0}} p$ | $6p \times 9 = \boxed{\phantom{0}} p$ |
| $8p \times 10 = \boxed{\phantom{0}} p$ | $3p \times 12 = \boxed{\phantom{0}} p$ | $7p \times 8 = \boxed{\phantom{0}} p$ |
| $5p \times 11 = \boxed{\phantom{0}} p$ | $9p \times 3 = \boxed{\phantom{0}} p$ | $5p \times 4 = \boxed{\phantom{0}} p$ |
| $9p \times 6 = \boxed{\phantom{0}} p$ | $11p \times 8 = \boxed{\phantom{0}} p$ | $12p \times 7 = \boxed{\phantom{0}} p$ |
| $3p \times 9 = \boxed{\phantom{0}} p$ | $8p \times 12 = \boxed{\phantom{0}} p$ | |
| $4p \times 7 = \boxed{\phantom{0}} p$ | $10p \times 8 = \boxed{\phantom{0}} p$ | $7p \times 9 = \boxed{\phantom{0}} p$ |
| $9p \times 4 = \boxed{\phantom{0}} p$ | $2p \times 12 = \boxed{\phantom{0}} p$ | $8p \times 5 = \boxed{\phantom{0}} p$ |
| $3p \times 11 = \boxed{\phantom{0}} p$ | $5p \times 3 = \boxed{\phantom{0}} p$ | $12p \times 2 = \boxed{\phantom{0}} p$ |
| $11p \times 7 = \boxed{\phantom{0}} p$ | $4p \times 9 = \boxed{\phantom{0}} p$ | $6p \times 6 = \boxed{\phantom{0}} p$ |

| 14p | 22p | 19p | 18p | 13p | 23p | 17p |
|---|---|---|---|---|---|---|
| ×5 | ×4 | ×3 | ×5 | ×7 | ×4 | ×3 |

| 17p | 12p | 19p | 23p | 16p | 34p |
|---|---|---|---|---|---|
| ×2 | ×7 | ×4 | ×3 | ×4 | ×2 |

**B**

| $4\overline{)96p}$ | $8\overline{)72p}$ | $3\overline{)81p}$ | $9\overline{)63p}$ | $6\overline{)84p}$ | $2\overline{)76p}$ | $5\overline{)95p}$ |
|---|---|---|---|---|---|---|

| $2\overline{)42p}$ | $4\overline{)76p}$ | $8\overline{)96p}$ | $6\overline{)78p}$ | $2\overline{)84p}$ | $6\overline{)72p}$ | $4\overline{)72p}$ |
|---|---|---|---|---|---|---|

| $3\overline{)48p}$ | $5\overline{)80p}$ | $7\overline{)84p}$ | $9\overline{)99p}$ | $5\overline{)65p}$ | $3\overline{)81p}$ | $7\overline{)91p}$ |
|---|---|---|---|---|---|---|

**C**
1 Find the cost of 6 pens at 12p each.
2 Four toys cost 92p. How much for each toy?
3 18p + 18p + 18p + 18p. Find the total by multiplication.
4 Six children share 84p. How much each?
5 One book costs 13p. What is the cost of **a** 4 books?　　　　**b** 6 books?
　**c** 3 books?　　　　**d** 7 books?　　　　**e** 2 books?
6 Share 1 fifty, 2 tens and 1 two equally among Ann, Peter, Eric and Tina.

# Pounds and pence

$$100p = £1·00$$

Complete

**A**     200p = £          500p = £          700p = £          600p = £
          900p = £          300p = £          800p = £          400p = £


**B**     104p  = £                    305p  = £                    143p  = £
          236p  = £                    624p  = £                    379p  = £
          476p  = £                    217p  = £                    914p  = £
          807p  = £                    763p  = £                    207p  = £


**C**     £3·45  = £   +   p                    £6·17 = £   +   p
          £7·06  = £   +   p                    £9·73 = £   +   p
          £12.14 = £   +   p                    £15·48 = £   +   p
          £2·72  = £   +   p                    £8·05 = £   +   p


**D**     £4·17 =   p                    £8·12 =   p                    £9·08 =   p
          £8·36 =   p                    £6·18 =   p                    £3·12 =   p
          £2·04 =   p                    £5·42 =   p                    £5·23 =   p
          £6·25 =   p                    £4·38 =   p                    £4·77 =   p


**E**                    £1·16  = £1 + 1 ten  + 6  ones
                         £2·72  = £   +   tens +   ones
                         £6·42  = £   +   tens +   ones
                         £9·04  = £   +   tens +   ones
                         £7·72  = £   +   tens +   ones
                         £8·96  = £   +   tens +   ones


**F**     How many 1p in
          £2·70?          £4·36?          £7·53?          £9·47?          £10·36?
          How many 10p in
          £9·20?          £3·40?          £2·50?          £6·70?          £8·30?

# Pounds and pence

**A**   Write as pence

£0·17       £0·27       £0·36       £0·76       £0·89       £0·05

**B**   Write as pounds

26p         7p          34p         8p          52p         5p

**C**   Write in figures, using the £ sign.

four pounds twenty-seven           seventy-six pence
one pound eighteen                 six pence
two pounds four                    ninety-six pence

**D**   Write in words

£7·45              £0·72              £14·04             £3·62

£0·12              £5·32              £9·26              £0·07

**E**   Write these amounts in order with the largest first.

£4·00          414p           47p            £4·36          £0·44

505p           £5·50          £5·27          59p            £0·61

£2·02          200p           22p            £22·00         £2·20

**F**   Add these amounts of money. Write your answer in pounds.

| 46p | 54p | 82p | 29p | 57p | 83p |
|---|---|---|---|---|---|
| + 63p | + 67p | + 34p | + 63p | + 72p | + 27p |

| 52p | 87p | 62p | 40p | 38p | 24p |
|---|---|---|---|---|---|
| + 18p | + 34p | + 53p | + 63p | + 61p | + 92p |

# Addition and subtraction — £ · p

**A**

| £0·17 | £0·48 | £0·63 | £0·53 | £0·56 |
|---|---|---|---|---|
| +£0·43 | +£0·37 | +£0·26 | +£0·29 | +£0·32 |

| £0·74 | £0·84 | £0·76 | £0·67 | £0·29 |
|---|---|---|---|---|
| +£0·32 | +£0·42 | +£0·57 | +£0·63 | +£0·94 |

| £4·07 | £5·18 | £6·42 | £8·02 | £5·34 |
|---|---|---|---|---|
| +£2·66 | +£3·82 | £2·97 | +£1·97 | +£7·69 |

| 2·02 | £2·11 | £1·48 | £6·16 | £0·85 |
|---|---|---|---|---|
| £3·54 | £4·30 | £5·86 | £3·58 | £7·47 |
| +£2·90 | +£0·63 | +£3·29 | +£0·47 | +£9·70 |

**B**

| £0·42 | £0·30 | £0·62 | £0·70 | £0·83 |
|---|---|---|---|---|
| −£0·37 | −£0·17 | −£0·34 | −£0·53 | −£0·54 |

| £1·63 | £1·29 | £1·53 | £1·27 | £1·03 |
|---|---|---|---|---|
| −£0·47 | −£0·69 | −£0·67 | −£0·64 | −£0·46 |

| £5·27 | £6·34 | £8·19 | £5·26 | £7·32 |
|---|---|---|---|---|
| −£3·19 | −£2·83 | −£5·19 | −£4·47 | −£6·29 |

**C**

Find the sum of £4·26, £0·47 and £2·32.

Find the difference between £6·07 and £3·29.

£12·46 add £3·52 add £0·47 add £0·20.

Six pounds ninety-two subtract eighty-four pence.

How much is £2·82 less than £10·06?

Find the total of £0·27, £6·29, £8·96.

# Multiplication — £ · p

**A**

| £0·18 | £0·24 | £0·32 | £0·47 | £0·15 |
|---|---|---|---|---|
| ×5 | ×4 | ×3 | ×2 | ×6 |

| £0·19 | £0·14 | £0·13 | £0·09 | £0·08 |
|---|---|---|---|---|
| ×5 | ×6 | ×7 | ×9 | ×11 |

| £0·53 | £0·76 | £0·38 | £0·26 | £0·64 |
|---|---|---|---|---|
| ×8 | ×6 | ×10 | ×12 | ×9 |

| £0·32 | £0·67 | £0·93 | £0·26 | £0·32 |
|---|---|---|---|---|
| ×9 | ×5 | ×7 | ×11 | ×12 |

| £1·43 | £2·76 | £3·07 | £4·32 | £1·59 |
|---|---|---|---|---|
| ×12 | ×10 | ×8 | ×9 | ×6 |

| £2·07 | £1·24 | £3·18 | £6·43 | £4·99 |
|---|---|---|---|---|
| ×3 | ×6 | ×7 | ×2 | ×9 |

**B**  
£4·22 × 3          £ 3·34 × 7  
£3·17 × 6          £12·16 × 9  
£2·18 × 9          £ 8·43 × 12

**C**  Find the product of  
£4·23 and 6          £2·20 and 8

**D**  Multiply  
£12·06 by 8          £9·26 by 3

**E**  Solve by multiplication  
£2·71 + £2·71 + £2·71          £0·27 + £0·27 + £0·27

# Division — £·p

**A**

| | | | | |
|---|---|---|---|---|
| 7)£0·42 | 4)£0·96 | 6)£0·84 | 5)£0·85 | 3)£0·87 |
| 6)£0·42 | 8)£0·96 | 4)£0·40 | 2)£0·92 | 10)£0·60 |
| 7)£0·84 | 5)£0·65 | 9)£0·81 | 11)£0·77 | 3)£0·78 |
| 12)£1·92 | 8)£1·84 | 3)£1·41 | 6)£0·72 | 9)£1·98 |
| 6)£1·56 | 10)£1·70 | 12)£1·80 | 8)£1·44 | 4)£1·28 |
| 3)£1·32 | 11)£1·87 | 5)£1·90 | 9)£1·98 | 7)£1·75 |
| 12)£52·32 | 7)£12·67 | 6)£8·34 | 11)£6·71 | 9)£10·80 |
| 8)£21·60 | 6)£19·02 | 2)£11·24 | 12)£47·16 | 4)£8·76 |
| 7)£34·30 | 11)£42·13 | 5)£14·35 | 9)£28·44 | 3)£8·43 |

**B**

| | |
|---|---|
| £11·52 ÷ 12 | £6·12 ÷ 9 |
| £55·15 ÷ 5 | £65·87 ÷ 7 |
| £2·34 ÷ 6 | £12·06 ÷ 3 |
| £3·04 ÷ 4 | £6·02 ÷ 2 |
| £73·70 ÷ 11 | £48·32 ÷ 8 |

**C**   Share   £33·04 by 7       Divide   £27·84 by 12
              £8·28 by 9                     £3·74 by 11
              £60·15 by 5                   £74·97 by  7

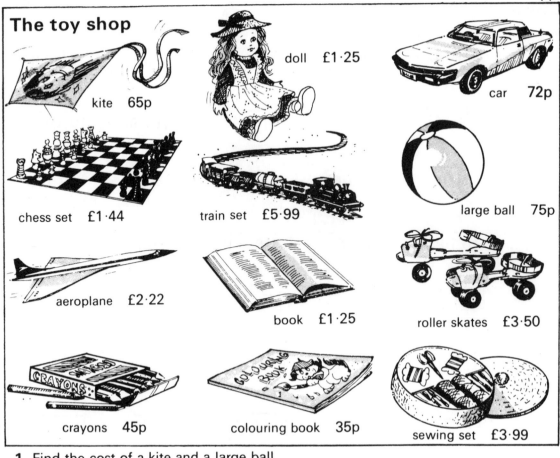

## The toy shop

doll £1·25

car 72p

kite 65p

chess set £1·44

train set £5·99

large ball 75p

aeroplane £2·22

book £1·25

roller skates £3·50

crayons 45p

colouring book 35p

sewing set £3·99

**1** Find the cost of a kite and a large ball.

**2** What is the total cost of an aeroplane, roller skates and a chess set?

**3** What would be the change from a £1·00 note after buying

   **a** a car?         **b** a large ball?         **c** crayons?

**4** How much dearer is the train set than the chess set?

**5** What is the cost of 3 pairs of roller skates?

**6** Find the cost of **a** 4 dolls       **b** 3 aeroplanes       **c** 4 cars

   **d** 5 kites       **e** 6 colouring books.

**7** What is the difference between the cost of an aeroplane and a sewing set?

**8** What change would I receive from £5·00 if I bought a book, crayons and a car?

**9** How many kites could I buy for £4·00 and what would my change be?

**10** Which would cost the most, 3 aeroplanes or 4 dolls?
    How much would the difference in price be?

# Capacity

**1 litre = 1000 ml**

 1000 ml   500 ml   250 ml   125 ml

**A**  How many millilitres in

**1** 1 l?     2 l?     4 l?     6 l?

9 l?     7 l?     3 l?     5 l?

$\frac{1}{2}$ l?     $\frac{1}{4}$ l?     $1\frac{1}{2}$ l?     $1\frac{1}{4}$ l?

$\frac{3}{4}$ l?     $2\frac{1}{4}$ l?     $2\frac{3}{4}$ l?     $1\frac{3}{4}$ l?

$$\frac{1}{10}\, l = 0.1\, l = 100\ ml$$

**2** 0·5 l?     0·4 l?     0·9 l?     0·7 l?

0·3 l?     0·8 l?     0·2 l?     0·1 l?

2·4 l?     1·6 l?     3·8 l?     4·5 l?

6·1 l?     5·3 l?     8·8 l?     2·7 l?

**B**  Write down **six** different ways you could fill the 1 litre container using the 500 ml, 250 ml and 125 ml containers.

**C**  Write down **three** ways you could fill the 500 ml container using the 250 ml and the 125 ml containers.

**D**

 600 ml   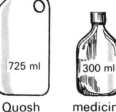 725 ml    300 ml   200 ml    325 ml    275 ml    250 ml

milk    Quosh    medicine    milk    lemonade    pop    wine

**1** Which two containers together hold $\frac{1}{2}$ litre?

**2** How many bottles of wine make a litre?

**3** Which two containers together would fill the 600 ml milk bottle?

**4** How much more does the Quosh bottle hold than the large milk bottle?

**5** How many small milk bottles would fill 2 medicine bottles?

**6** Which 3 containers together hold the same as the Quosh bottle?

# Length — m and cm

**1 metre = 100 cm**

**A**    Change to cm

| | | | | |
|---|---|---|---|---|
| 2 m | 9 m | 6 m | 4 m | 7 m |
| 12 m | 16 m | | | |

**B**    Change to m

| | | | | |
|---|---|---|---|---|
| 400 cm | 300 cm | 500 cm | 100 cm | 800 cm |
| 1300 cm | | | | |

**C**    Complete

| | | |
|---|---|---|
| $\frac{1}{2}$ m =   cm | $\frac{1}{4}$ m =   cm | $\frac{3}{4}$ m =   cm |
| $2\frac{1}{2}$ m =   cm | $1\frac{1}{4}$ m =   cm | $1\frac{3}{4}$ m =   cm |
| $4\frac{1}{2}$ m =   cm | $2\frac{1}{4}$ m =   cm | $2\frac{3}{4}$ m =   cm |
| $6\frac{1}{2}$ m =   cm | $4\frac{1}{4}$ m =   cm | $7\frac{3}{4}$ m =   cm |

**D**

| | | |
|---|---|---|
| 50 cm =   m | 25 cm =   m | 75 cm =   m |
| 350 cm =   m | 525 cm =   m | 375 cm =   m |
| 150 cm =   m | 325 cm =   m | 475 cm =   m |

**E**

| | |
|---|---|
| 1 m 23 cm =   cm | 2 m 16 cm =   cm |
| 4 m 5 cm =   cm | 3 m 8 cm =   cm |
| 9 m 36 cm =   cm | 8 m 29 cm =   cm |

**F**

| | |
|---|---|
| 225 cm =   m   cm | 518 cm =   m   cm |
| 312 cm =   m   cm | 654 cm =   m   cm |
| 806 cm =   m   cm | 931 cm =   m   cm |

**321 cm = 3·21 m**

**G**    Complete

| | | |
|---|---|---|
| 532 cm =   m | 196 cm =   m | 92 cm =   m |
| 402 cm =   m | 52 cm =   m | 307 cm =   m |
| 390 cm =   m | 7 cm =   m | 1426 cm =   m |
| 4·26 m =   cm | 8·16 m =   cm | 10·27 m =   cm |
| 12·06 m =   cm | 0·09 m =   cm | 3·41 m =   cm |
| 0·27 m =   cm | 0·77 m =   cm | 1·01 m =   cm |

**H**    Write as decimals

| | | | | |
|---|---|---|---|---|
| $\frac{1}{2}$ m | $\frac{1}{4}$ m | $\frac{3}{4}$ m | $\frac{1}{100}$ m | $\frac{23}{100}$ m |
| $\frac{47}{100}$ m | $1\frac{11}{100}$ m | $2\frac{29}{100}$ m | | |

# Length — m, cm and mm

**10 mm = 1 cm**

**A**
| | | |
|---|---|---|
| 50 mm =   cm | 40 mm =   cm | 60 mm =   cm |
| 30 mm =   cm | 90 mm =   cm | 20 mm =   cm |
| 130 mm =   cm | 220 mm =   cm | 190 mm =   cm |

**B**
| | | |
|---|---|---|
| 7 cm =   mm | 8 cm =   mm | 9 cm =   mm |
| 6 cm =   mm | 5 cm =   mm | 3 cm =   mm |
| 15 cm =   mm | 320 cm =   mm | 530 cm =   mm |

**27 mm = 2 cm 7 mm = 2·7 cm**

**C** Complete

| | | |
|---|---|---|
| 53 mm =   cm   mm =   cm | | 7 mm =   cm   mm =   cm |
| 86 mm =   cm   mm =   cm | | 4 mm =   cm   mm =   cm |
| 131 mm =   cm   mm =   cm | | 6 mm =   cm   mm =   cm |
| 268 mm =   cm   mm =   cm | | |
| 320 mm =   cm   mm =   cm | | |

**D** Change to mm

| | | | |
|---|---|---|---|
| 4·1 cm | 3·7 cm | 0·9 cm | 0·8 cm |
| 14·2 cm | 5·6 cm | | |

**1000 mm = 1 metre**   **7340 mm = 7·340 m**

**E** Complete

| | | |
|---|---|---|
| 7000 mm =   m | 9000 mm =   m | 3000 mm =   m |
| 4500 mm =   m | 2500 mm =   m | 8500 mm =   m |
| 5250 mm =   m | 8250 mm =   m | 1250 mm =   m |
| 9750 mm =   m | 3750 mm =   m | 4750 mm =   m |

**F** Change to mm

| | | | |
|---|---|---|---|
| $6\frac{1}{2}$ m | $5\frac{1}{2}$ m | $3\frac{1}{2}$ m | $2\frac{3}{4}$ m |
| $1\frac{3}{4}$ m | $4\frac{1}{4}$ m | $7\frac{1}{4}$ m | $9\frac{1}{4}$ m |

**G** Complete

| | | |
|---|---|---|
| 6670 mm =   m   mm | 5026 mm =   m   mm | 2340 mm =   m   mm |
| 8026 mm =   m   mm | 2726 mm =   m   mm | 8791 mm =   m   mm |

**H**
| | | |
|---|---|---|
| 4 m 135 mm =   mm | 6 m 296 mm =   mm | 8 m 196 mm =   mm |
| 16 m 176 mm =   mm | 5 m 17 mm =   mm | 9 m 5 mm =   mm |

# The kilometre    1 km = 1000 m

**A**    Change to metres

| | | |
|---|---|---|
| 1 km 275 m | 3 km 536 m | 4 km 326 m |
| 8 km 824 m | 2 km 56 m | 7 km 36 m |
| 5 km 4 m | 6 km 8 m | $4\frac{1}{2}$ km    $3\frac{1}{4}$ km |
| $2\frac{3}{4}$ km | $9\frac{1}{2}$ km | |

**B**    Write as km and m

| | | |
|---|---|---|
| 3760 m | 2430 m | 1641 m |
| 8252 m | 5862 m | 4026 m |
| 7054 m | 1006 m | 3002 m    6008 m |

# Perimeter

**C**    Measure the sides of these shapes, then write

   **a** the length    **b** the width    **c** the perimeter.

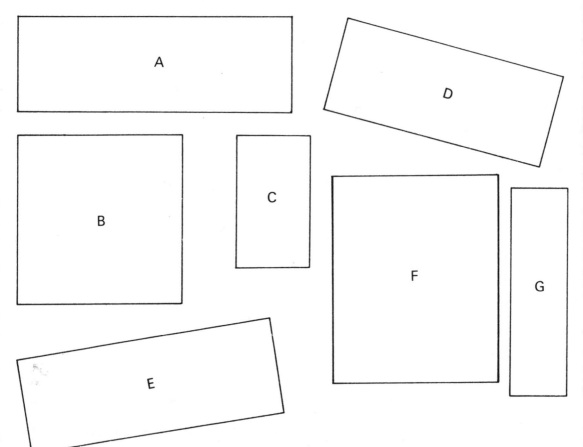

# Area

**A** Find the area of these shapes.

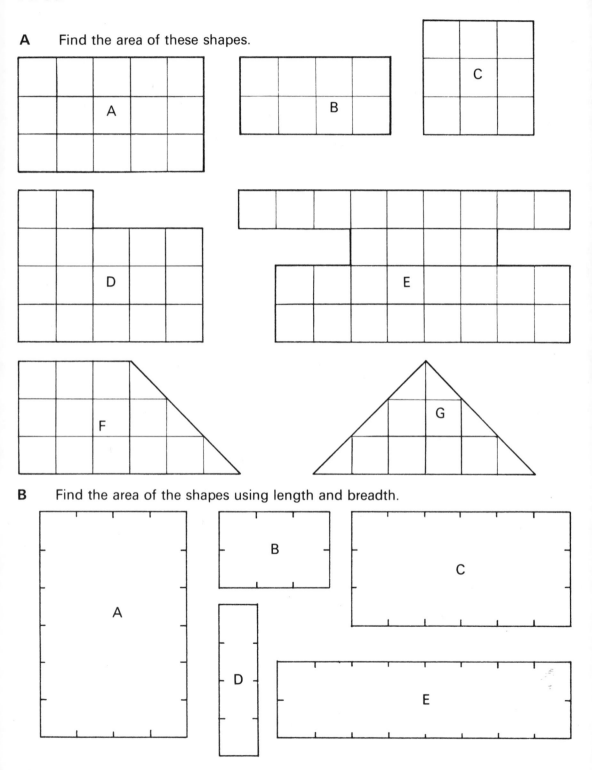

**B** Find the area of the shapes using length and breadth.

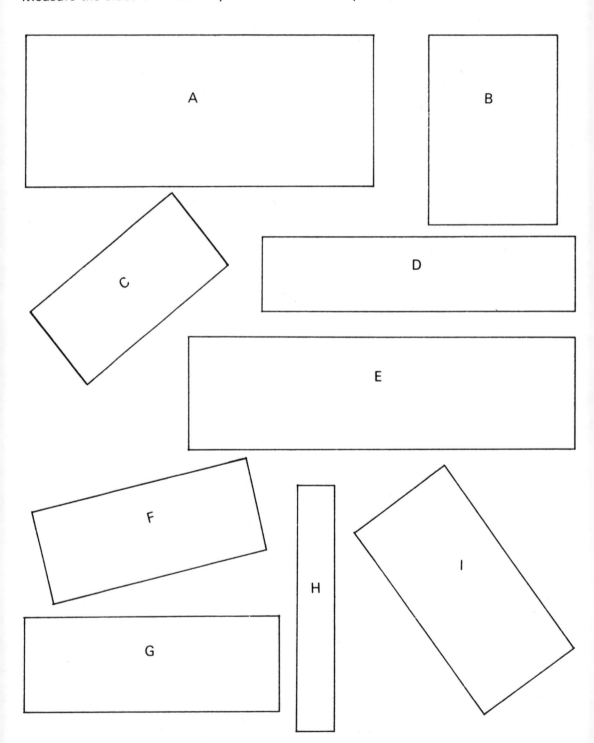

# Area and perimeter

Measure the sides of these shapes then find **a** the perimeter    **b** the area.

A

B

C

D

E

F

H

I

G

# Scale measurement

**A**  Each of these objects has been drawn to a scale of 1 cm to 2 cm. Write the **actual** length of each object.

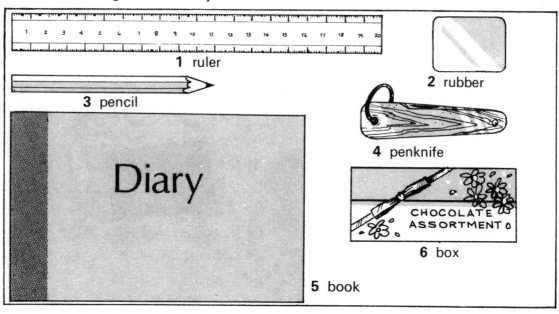

1 ruler

2 rubber

3 pencil

4 penknife

Diary

CHOCOLATE
ASSORTMENT

6 box

5 book

**B**  Using the scale 1 cm to 2 cm draw lines to represent

20 cm               30 cm               18 cm               14 cm               6 cm

12 cm

**C**  The scale is 1 cm to 5 cm. What length do each of these lines represent?

**D**  The scale is 1 cm to 10 cm. What length of line would you draw to represent these distances?

45 cm               60 cm               55 cm               20 cm               50 cm

25 cm

**E**  The scale is 1 cm to 4 km. How far apart are towns A and B?

A ⊙————————————————————————————————⊙ B

# Scales and maps

**A**

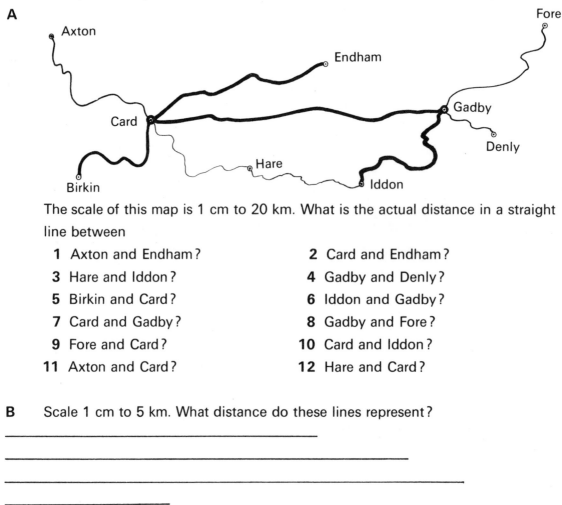

The scale of this map is 1 cm to 20 km. What is the actual distance in a straight line between

1 Axton and Endham?

2 Card and Endham?

3 Hare and Iddon?

4 Gadby and Denly?

5 Birkin and Card?

6 Iddon and Gadby?

7 Card and Gadby?

8 Gadby and Fore?

9 Fore and Card?

10 Card and Iddon?

11 Axton and Card?

12 Hare and Card?

**B** Scale 1 cm to 5 km. What distance do these lines represent?

What length of line would represent these distances?

15 km       40 km       25 km       60 km       $17\frac{1}{2}$ km

$52\frac{1}{2}$ km

**C** Measure these lines then find the scale which has been used.

8 m

6 km

2 km

3 m

3 km

# Mass

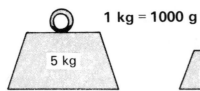

1 kg = 1000 g

5 kg

2 kg

**A**  How many of each of the following weights would it take to balance
**a** 5 kg?  **b** 2 kg?

500 g      200 g      100 g      50 g      20 g      10 g

**B**  How many grams in

2 kg?          8½ kg?          6½ kg?          10 kg?

3½ kg?          7 kg?

**C**  How many kilograms in

4000 g?          6000 g?          8500 g?          2500 g?

5000 g?          3500 g?

**D**  Write the following as kg and g.

4260 g                8120 g                2050 g

3160 g                7005 g

**E**  Write as grams

2 kg 360 g          3 kg 115 g          5 kg 70 g

4 kg 33 g          6 kg 5 g

**F**  Write as grams

3·2 kg          4·1 kg          6·3 kg          5·4 kg

8·6 kg

**G**  How much less than ½ kg are each of these weights?

436 g          229 g          347 g          291 g          32 g

67 g

**H**  How much greater than 2 kg are

3 kg 471 g?          2 kg 126 g?          4021 g?

11 kg 741 g?          8006 g?          Give your answers in kg and g.

**I**  Balance these equations.

4 kg 200 g + 800 g =          + 3 kg 250 g

700 g + 200 g + 300 g =          − 200 g

+ 3 kg + 500 g = 4 kg + 600 g

6 kg −          = 2 kg 300 g − 1 kg 800 g

200 g + 800 g + 3 kg 100 g = 4 kg 50 g +

# Comparison — other measures

1 Three oranges weigh 500 g. How many oranges in a sack weighing 50 kg?

2 A barrel holds 300 litres of vinegar. How much will be left after 25 bottles each holding 500 ml have been filled?

3 How many 80 cm lengths can be cut from a 5 m length of wood? What length of wood is left?

4 A jar holds 450 ml. How many litres in 12 jars?

5 A box contains 36 blocks of chocolate each weighing 100 g. What is the total weight if the box weighs 50 g? Answer in kg.

6 How many 250 g packs of butter can be weighed from $8\frac{1}{2}$ kg?

7 A rope is cut into 6 equal parts of 75 cm. How long was the length of rope in metres?

8 A car used 4 litres of petrol on a journey of 50 km. How many litres are used on a journey of 725 km?

9 How many 200 ml bottles can be filled from a 50 litre tank of milk?

10 How many 50 g bags of sweets can be weighed from a 5 kg box?

11 A sack holds 50 kg of potatoes. How many 2 kg bags can be made from it?

12 A milk bottle holds 600 ml. If a family has 2 bottles of milk each day, how many litres do they drink in a week?

13 How long are 8 pencils if one pencil is 17 cm long?

14 Four lengths of cloth each $2\frac{1}{4}$ m long are cut from a roll of cloth 20 m long. How many more lengths of $2\frac{1}{4}$ m can be cut from it?

15 A $\frac{1}{4}$ of a fruit cake weighs 425 g. How much does the whole cake weigh? Answer in kg.

16 A boy's stride is 50 cm. How many steps does he take to cover 100 metres?

17 If ten sweets weigh 50 g, what would 210 sweets weigh? Answer in kg.

18 A medicine spoon holds 5 ml. How many doses are there in a 300 ml bottle?

19 12 balls of wool each weighing 25 g are needed to knit a girl's cardigan. How much wool is needed to knit 5 cardigans? Answer in kg.

20 a How many ribbons each measuring 12 cm can be cut from a 4 m roll?
   b What length of ribbon will be left?

# Shopping

Find the cost of the following amounts.

**1** 1 litre costs 80p    **a** 4 litres    **b** 6 litres    **c** 10 litres    **d** 9 litres

**2** $\frac{1}{2}$ litre costs 10p    **a** $\frac{1}{4}$ litre    **b** $1\frac{1}{4}$ litres    **c** $4\frac{1}{2}$ litres    **d** 6 litres

**3** 400 ml cost 32p    **a** 100 ml    **b** 600 ml    **c** 700 ml    **d** 900 ml

**4** 600 ml cost 60p    **a** 900 ml    **b** 400 ml    **c** 450 ml    **d** 750 ml

**5** 500 ml cost 16p    **a** $2\frac{1}{2}$ l    **b** 3 l    **c** $\frac{1}{4}$ l    **d** $1\frac{1}{4}$ l

**6** $\frac{1}{4}$ litre costs 15p    **a** $\frac{3}{4}$ l    **b** $\frac{1}{2}$ l    **c** $4\frac{1}{4}$ l    **d** $2\frac{3}{4}$ l

**7** $\frac{1}{2}$ metre costs £1·25    **a** 5 m    **b** $8\frac{1}{2}$ m    **c** 6 m    **d** $3\frac{1}{2}$ m

**8** $\frac{1}{2}$ metre costs 60p    **a** $\frac{1}{4}$ m    **b** $2\frac{1}{4}$ m    **c** $3\frac{1}{2}$ m    **d** 5 m

**9** 1 metre costs 96p    **a** 3 m    **b** $2\frac{1}{2}$ m    **c** 5 m    **d** 7 m

**10** $\frac{1}{4}$ metre costs 12p    **a** 1 m    **b** $\frac{1}{2}$ m    **c** $2\frac{1}{2}$ m    **d** $3\frac{1}{4}$ m

**11** $\frac{3}{4}$ metre costs 33p    **a** $\frac{1}{4}$ m    **b** 1 m    **c** $5\frac{1}{2}$ m    **d** $2\frac{1}{4}$ m

**12** $\frac{1}{4}$ metre costs 35p    **a** $4\frac{1}{2}$ m    **b** $1\frac{1}{4}$ m    **c** 3 m    **d** 6 m

**13** $\frac{1}{2}$ kg costs 35p    **a** $2\frac{1}{2}$ kg    **b** $1\frac{1}{2}$ kg    **c** $3\frac{1}{2}$ kg    **d** 5 kg

**14** $\frac{1}{2}$ kg costs 16p    **a** $\frac{1}{4}$ kg    **b** $5\frac{1}{2}$ kg    **c** $6\frac{1}{4}$ kg    **d** 7 kg

**15** 500 g cost 25p    **a** 100 g    **b** 700 g    **c** 900 g    **d** 300 g

**16** 250 g cost 7p    **a** 1 kg    **b** $1\frac{1}{2}$ kg    **c** $2\frac{1}{4}$ kg    **d** 4 kg

**17** 200 g cost 12p    **a** 400 g    **b** 500 g    **c** 1 kg    **d** $1\frac{1}{4}$ kg

**18** 100 g cost 4p    **a** 1 kg    **b** 400 g    **c** 700 g    **d** $5\frac{1}{2}$ kg

# Time — revision

**A**   Write the times shown on these clocks.

**B**   Write the times shown on these clocks in two ways.

**C**   Draw clocks to show these times.

| | | |
|---|---|---|
| ten past six | five to nine | $\frac{1}{4}$ past eight |
| 35 minutes past two | $\frac{1}{2}$ past one | 40 minutes past three |
| $\frac{1}{4}$ to twelve | twenty past five | ten to four |
| 50 minutes past seven | twenty-five past eleven | five past ten |
| two o'clock | 20 minutes to three | 25 minutes to six |

# Time — am and pm

**A**   Write these times using figures only.

10 minutes past 6          quarter to nine          10 minutes to 4

quarter past eight          20 minutes to 5          5 minutes to 10

**B**   Write the times shown on these clocks using figures only.

**C**   Write these times using **am** or **pm**.

**morning times**

**afternoon and evening times**

**D**   Write these times in figures using **am** or **pm**.

25 minutes to one in the afternoon

20 minutes past six in the afternoon

10 minutes to four in the morning

quarter to eight in the evening

25 minutes past twelve in the morning

5 minutes to nine in the evening

quarter past two in the morning

10 minutes past eleven in the evening

5 minutes past three in the afternoon

half past five in the morning

# Time in minutes

## A

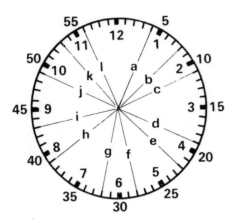

Write the number of minutes shown by each of the pointers.

a    b    c

d    e    f

g    h    i

j    k    l

## B Write the time shown on each of these clocks in figures.

## C Write the times shown on each clock in figures using am or pm.

morning     evening     afternoon     morning

# Adjusting times

**A**     Each clock is 10 minutes slow. What is the correct time?

**B**     Each clock is 10 minutes fast. What is the correct time?

**C**     How many minutes must pass for these clocks to show 10 o'clock?

**D**

| A | B | C | D |
|---|---|---|---|
|  | |  |  |

How many minutes have passed between clocks

A and B?               B and C?

A and C?               B and D?

A and D?               C and D?

# Time — problems

**A**    Here are the times of the bus between Porton and Fartown. Answer the questions.

| town | time |
|------|------|
| Porton | 8·15 |
| Benford | 8·39 |
| Markham | 8·57 |
| Southam | 9·20 |
| Fartown | 9·55 |

**1** How long does the journey from Porton to Fartown take?

**2** How long from Porton to Benford?

**3** How long from Porton to Markham?

**4** How long from Porton to Southam?

**5** Between which two towns does the journey take the least time?

**6** Between which two towns does the journey take the most time?

**B**    Find how many hours and minutes between these times.

8·00 and 10·30             0·55 and 1·25

7·36 and 7·55              3·29 and 3·51

2·29 and 3·42             11·23 and 12·06

3·31 and 5·26              1·42 and 4·03

**C**    How many minutes in

$1\frac{1}{2}$ h?        $1\frac{1}{4}$ h?        $2\frac{1}{2}$ h?        $4\frac{1}{2}$ h?

$1\frac{3}{4}$ h?        $2\frac{1}{4}$ h?        $2\frac{3}{4}$ h?

**D**    A TV programme starts at 5·40 pm and lasts for 45 min. What time does it end?

**E**    John's watch says 2·55. If it is a quarter of an hour slow, what is the correct time?

**F**    School starts at 9·00 am. Peter leaves home at 8·55 am and is 3 minutes late. How long did he take to reach school?

**G**    Lunchtime at school lasts from 12·00 pm to 1·15 pm.

    **1** How many minutes is this?

    **2** If afternoon school lasts $2\frac{1}{2}$ h, what time does school close?

# The calendar

### January

| Su | M | Tu | W | Th | F | S |
|---|---|---|---|---|---|---|
| | 1 | 2 | 3 | 4 | 5 | 6 |
| 7 | 8 | 9 | 10 | 11 | 12 | 13 |
| 14 | 15 | 16 | 17 | 18 | 19 | 20 |
| 21 | 22 | 23 | 24 | 25 | 26 | 27 |
| 28 | 29 | 30 | 31 | | | |

### February

| Su | M | Tu | W | Th | F | S |
|---|---|---|---|---|---|---|
| | | | | | 1 | 2 | 3 |
| 4 | 5 | 6 | 7 | 8 | 9 | 10 |
| 11 | 12 | 13 | 14 | 15 | 16 | 17 |
| 18 | 19 | 20 | 21 | 22 | 23 | 24 |
| 25 | 26 | 27 | 28 | | | |

### March

| Su | M | Tu | W | Th | F | S |
|---|---|---|---|---|---|---|
| | | | | 1 | 2 | 3 |
| 4 | 5 | 6 | 7 | 8 | 9 | 10 |
| 11 | 12 | 13 | 14 | 15 | 16 | 17 |
| 18 | 19 | 20 | 21 | 22 | 23 | 24 |
| 25 | 26 | 27 | 28 | 29 | 30 | 31 |

### April

| Su | M | Tu | W | Th | F | S |
|---|---|---|---|---|---|---|
| 1 | 2 | 3 | 4 | 5 | 6 | 7 |
| 8 | 9 | 10 | 11 | 12 | 13 | 14 |
| 15 | 16 | 17 | 18 | 19 | 20 | 21 |
| 22 | 23 | 24 | 25 | 26 | 27 | 28 |
| 29 | 30 | | | | | |

### May

| Su | M | Tu | W | Th | F | S |
|---|---|---|---|---|---|---|
| | 1 | 2 | 3 | 4 | 5 | |
| 6 | 7 | 8 | 9 | 10 | 11 | 12 |
| 13 | 14 | 15 | 16 | 17 | 18 | 19 |
| 20 | 21 | 22 | 23 | 24 | 25 | 26 |
| 27 | 28 | 29 | 30 | 31 | | |

### June

| Su | M | Tu | W | Th | F | S |
|---|---|---|---|---|---|---|
| | | | | | 1 | 2 |
| 3 | 4 | 5 | 6 | 7 | 8 | 9 |
| 10 | 11 | 12 | 13 | 14 | 15 | 16 |
| 17 | 18 | 19 | 20 | 21 | 22 | 23 |
| 24 | 25 | 26 | 27 | 28 | 29 | 30 |

### July

| Su | M | Tu | W | Th | F | S |
|---|---|---|---|---|---|---|
| 1 | 2 | 3 | 4 | 5 | 6 | 7 |
| 8 | 9 | 10 | 11 | 12 | 13 | 14 |
| 15 | 16 | 17 | 18 | 19 | 20 | 21 |
| 22 | 23 | 24 | 25 | 26 | 27 | 28 |
| 29 | 30 | 31 | | | | |

### August

| Su | M | Tu | W | Th | F | S |
|---|---|---|---|---|---|---|
| | | | 1 | 2 | 3 | 4 |
| 5 | 6 | 7 | 8 | 9 | 10 | 11 |
| 12 | 13 | 14 | 15 | 16 | 17 | 18 |
| 19 | 20 | 21 | 22 | 23 | 24 | 25 |
| 26 | 27 | 28 | 29 | 30 | 31 | |

### September

| Su | M | Tu | W | Th | F | S |
|---|---|---|---|---|---|---|
| | | | | | | 1 |
| 2 | 3 | 4 | 5 | 6 | 7 | 8 |
| 9 | 10 | 11 | 12 | 13 | 14 | 15 |
| 16 | 17 | 18 | 19 | 20 | 21 | 22 |
| 23 | 24 | 25 | 26 | 27 | 28 | 29 |
| 30 | | | | | | |

### October

| Su | M | Tu | W | Th | F | S |
|---|---|---|---|---|---|---|
| | 1 | 2 | 3 | 4 | 5 | 6 |
| 7 | 8 | 9 | 10 | 11 | 12 | 13 |
| 14 | 15 | 16 | 17 | 18 | 19 | 20 |
| 21 | 22 | 23 | 24 | 25 | 26 | 27 |
| 28 | 29 | 30 | 31 | | | |

### November

| Su | M | Tu | W | Th | F | S |
|---|---|---|---|---|---|---|
| | | | | 1 | 2 | 3 |
| 4 | 5 | 6 | 7 | 8 | 9 | 10 |
| 11 | 12 | 13 | 14 | 15 | 16 | 17 |
| 18 | 19 | 20 | 21 | 22 | 23 | 24 |
| 25 | 26 | 27 | 28 | 29 | 30 | |

### December

| Su | M | Tu | W | Th | F | S |
|---|---|---|---|---|---|---|
| | | | | | | 1 |
| 2 | 3 | 4 | 5 | 6 | 7 | 8 |
| 9 | 10 | 11 | 12 | 13 | 14 | 15 |
| 16 | 17 | 18 | 19 | 20 | 21 | 22 |
| 23 | 24 | 25 | 26 | 27 | 28 | 29 |
| 30 | 31 | | | | | |

1 Is this year a leap year? How do you know?

2 Which 4 months have 5 Fridays in them?

3 Which 2 months begin on the first day of the week?

4 Name the 2 months which end on Saturday.

5 Jane is six months younger than Mark. Mark's birthday is in December. When is Jane's birthday?

6 Jane's school went on an outing on the third Wednesday of the sixth month. What date was this?

7 Dances were held on the second Saturday of each month. Give the dates of the 12 dances this year.

8 Give the day on which each month with 31 days ends.

9 Give the day on which each month with 30 days begins.

10 On what day was New Year's Day?

11 On what day will New Year's Day next year be?

12 On what day was Christmas Day?

# Graphs

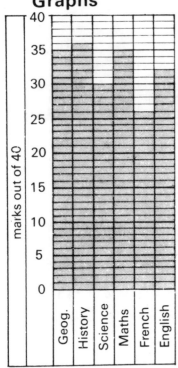

**A** The graph shows how many marks Peter gained in his examinations. Copy and complete this table.

| Subject | Geog. | History | Science | Maths | French | English |
|---------|-------|---------|---------|-------|--------|---------|
| mark    |       |         |         |       |        |         |

**1** In which subject did he gain highest marks?

**2** Which subject was his worst?

**3** In which subjects did he gain the same marks?

**4** In which subject did he gain $\frac{3}{4}$ marks?

**5** What was the difference between his highest mark and his lowest mark?

**6** What were the total possible marks?

**7** What was Peter's total mark?

**8** How many marks did he lose altogether?

**B**                    **Brownhill school**

Each child in the school chose their favourite sports game.
Hockey, netball and rounders were for girls.
Rugby, cricket and football were for boys.
How many voted for each game?

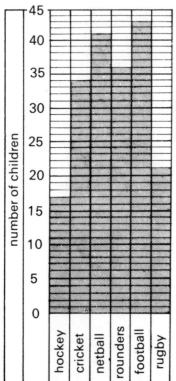

| hockey | cricket | netball | rounders | football | rugby |
|--------|---------|---------|----------|----------|-------|
|        |         |         |          |          |       |

**1** How many boys voted?

**2** How many girls voted?

**3** How many children voted altogether?

**4** There are 200 children in the school. How many were absent?

**5** What was the boys' favourite game?

**6** What was the girls' favourite game?

**7** How many chose rugby or football?

**8** How many chose hockey or rounders?

**9** Which game received the least votes?

**10** How many more boys voted than girls?

# Graphs

## A

|  | 0 | 5 | 10 | 15 |
|---|---|---|---|---|
| Heaton | | | | |
| Warcombe | | | | |
| Corm | | | | |
| Birford | | | | |
| Forham | | | | |
| Wessex | | | | |
| Imford | | | | |
| Frame | | | | |

**Schools football**

This is a record of the football matches played between eight school teams, showing the matches won.

1 Which team won the most matches?

2 Which team won the fewest matches?

3 Which teams won the same number of matches?

4 Which two teams together won the same number of matches as Warcombe?

5 How many more matches did Heaton win than Birford?

6 Which two teams together won as many matches as Imford and Warcombe?

## B  High school attendance — Monday

Children present

|  | 0 | 10 | 20 | 30 |
|---|---|---|---|---|
| class 1 | | | | |
| class 2 | | | | |
| class 3 | | | | |
| class 4 | | | | |
| class 5 | | | | |
| class 6 | | | | |

Each class has 30 children.

1 How many children are there in the school?

2 How many children were absent on Monday?

3 Which class had the most absences?

4 Which class had full attendance?

## C

Draw your own graphs for these tables, done by a group of children about their class.

**1 Pets**

| horse | rabbit | dog | cat | fish | hamster |
|---|---|---|---|---|---|
| 2 | 9 | 15 | 6 | 5 | 3 |

**2 Drinks**

| orange | coke | lemon | milk | tea |
|---|---|---|---|---|
| 10 | 18 | 5 | 4 | 3 |

# Answers

## Page 2 Revision – addition
A 78, 79, 89, 99, 89, 98, 98
B 989, 799, 989, 999, 899, 988, 879
C 98, 87, 109, 80, 102, 96, 88
D 894, 986, 993, 798, 898, 796, 999
E 176, 199, 189, 208, 219, 179, 169
F 947, 956, 968, 768, 979, 959, 828
G 131, 143, 155, 154, 137, 145, 193
H 652, 769, 785, 922, 802, 856, 888

## Page 3 Addition – thousands
A 1697, 1399, 1599, 1478, 1979, 1589
B 1458, 1758, 1799, 1403, 1744, 1287
C 1619, 1619, 1958, 1166, 1714, 1448
D 2439, 2764, 2251, 2193, 2243, 2244
E 2035, 1983, 2128, 2204, 2257, 2105
F 2072, 2364, 2637, 2073, 2533, 2201
G 4489, 4749, 9058, 9749, 7648
H 8311, 8929, 9556, 8663, 9697

## Page 4 Revision – subtraction
A 542, 517, 523, 816, 121, 251
B 301, 601, 101, 302, 401, 401
C 200, 300, 100, 400, 100, 400
D 313, 422, 504, 515, 423, 311
E 171, 344, 33, 151, 112, 120
F 209, 416, 212, 419, 318, 408
G 193, 153, 253, 494, 193, 273
H 95, 288, 279, 165, 368, 98
I 127, 214, 8, 33, 211, 41
J 119, 269, 159, 238, 178, 158
K 8, 25, 9, 25;   16, 37, 7, 23;
8, 44, 13, 20

## Page 5 Subtraction – thousands
A 524, 624, 121, 243, 313, 711
B 736, 913, 644, 824, 947, 724
C 883, 891, 883, 775, 274, 671
D 899, 887, 669, 776, 775, 456
E 649, 529, 476, 128, 266, 569
F 565, 733, 125, 508, 186, 542
G 1556, 1618, 4142, 606, 1322, 3293
H 559, 1234, 3671, 5848, 2957, 4728
I 1468, 3274, 4153, 346, 3641, 371
J 1266, 1489, 5077, 1375, 5579, 893
K 47, 43, 18, 29;   35, 9, 27, 9;
25, 15, 28, 37

## Page 6 Notation
A 8 thousands, 3 tens, 4 hundreds,
6 units, 2 hundreds;
2 tens, 4 thousands, 6 units, 5 hundreds,
1 ten
B 620, 60;    850, 85;    115, 90;
710, 200;    6054, 49;    3006, 906
C four thousand and seven,
seven hundred and ninety-three,
one hundred and fifteen,
five hundred and five,
nine thousand six hundred and twenty,
twenty;
thirty,  four hundred and two,
five hundred and thirty,
one hundred and seven,
three thousand and seventeen,
nine hundred and ninety-nine
D 100, 410, 421, 1200;    119, 142, 59, 1229;
203, 2300, 196, 1003;    93, 164, 3067, 696;
1041, 2404, 1821, 374;    472, 2241, 4731,
1900

## Page 7 Addition and subtraction
A 3794, 1917, 2205, 3746, 7838;
9161, 2819, 3279, 6388, 4471
B 3902, 712;    1055, 325;    8365, 2017;
662, 3202;    334, 5229;    3645, 5772
C 4587, 3724, 4776, 1030, 7949
D 584, 205, 930, 3303, 378

## Page 8 Multiplication – revision
A 848, 336, 488, 999, 966, 848
B 510, 642, 832, 618, 618, 636
C 681, 692, 595, 690, 585, 496
D 780, 906, 688, 955, 728, 849
E 582, 702, 996, 945, 876, 534
F 2250, 1850, 1172, 2238, 1196, 3894
G 7355, 7086, 6500, 6378, 3098
H 5444, 7015, 4694, 5820;
4776, 5395, 6998, 5994
I 1380, 380;    5096, 572;    2376, 588
J 615, 1400, 576

## Page 9 Multiplication by 7
A 21, 14, 28, 42, 63;    84, 35, 56, 21, 14;
7, 70, 49, 42, 35;    0, 28, 77
B 27, 19, 31, 39;    65, 54, 44, 61;
24, 45, 60, 20;    33, 53, 37, 69;
25, 62, 67, 34;    16, 38, 52

C 2982, 2772, 3199, 1309, 4263, 1036;
2268, 4445, 2086, 3073, 1239, 1456;
8645, 9723, 8232, 7476, 9821
D 3311, 4403, 5656, 6503;
8001, 7602, 8435, 7679
E 3479, 3563, 609, 2653, 672, 2170

## Page 10 Multiplication by 8
A 2, 8, 3, 6, 12;   0, 4, 7, 5, 11;
8, 3, 6, 4, 10;   2, 9, 1, 7, 5
B 70, 50, 23, 30, 10;   63, 51, 12, 62, 71;
53, 14, 60, 31, 52;   21, 15, 22, 54, 13;
20, 55, 61, 11
C 2616, 3272, 4944, 4160, 7896, 3448;
4848, 7176, 4256, 1360, 4376, 6584;
8784, 9672, 8560, 9320, 9144
D 3040, 5400, 7912, 1648;
9192, 8552, 8048, 8992
E 3176, 8216, 5832;
3512, 8200, 7432, 5040, 6688, 8072, 4848

## Page 11 Multiplication by 9
A 9, 36, 54, 63, 0;   45, 72, 36, 108, 81;
63, 27, 99, 18, 18;   0, 45, 72, 90, 27;   54
B 11, 43, 42, 31, 40;   15, 71, 70, 35, 81;   36,
25, 33, 12, 61;   44, 34, 54, 80, 32;
14, 24, 18, 23, 41;   50, 72, 22, 17, 51;
53, 62, 27, 60, 63;   26, 16, 40, 20, 52;
30, 13, 45, 10, 21
C 3843, 6147, 8451, 1413, 6372, 4734;   5679,
6840, 8181, 3474, 7425, 3879;
9684, 9963, 9315, 9972

D

| 4 6 | 8 0 9 | 2 5 3 | 1 0 4 5 |
|---|---|---|---|
| x 9 | x 9 | x 9 | x 9 |
| 4 1 4 | 7 2 8 1 | 2 2 7 7 | 9 4 0 5 |

## Page 12 Multiplication by 11
A 77, 44, 33, 11, 99;   88, 22, 66, 55, 0;
8, 4, 5, 1, 6;   3, 7, 0, 9, 2
B 81, 96, 51, 82, 72;   80, 42, 83, 97, 64;   73,
94, 84, 61, 108;   95, 107, 40, 75, 31;   60, 30,
86, 74, 62;   106, 63, 71, 104, 91;   41, 85,
53, 105, 52;   101, 92, 102, 93, 90;   100, 20,
70, 50, 103
C 2585, 4444, 7458, 1892, 3157, 3916;   1540,
9966, 9075, 8052, 6864, 4202
D 4037, 5577, 1540

## Page 13 Multiplication by 12
A 48, 108, 60, 36, 12;   0, 24, 96, 84, 72;
1, 5, 7, 3, 9;   4, 6, 2, 0, 8

B 41, 21, 111, 80, 42;   112, 92, 31, 110, 53;
100, 51, 30, 50, 102;   101, 52, 32, 104, 55;
116, 20, 115, 81, 40;   93, 56, 44, 33, 114;
117, 105, 90, 54, 103;   45, 57, 91, 113, 43
C 8712, 5400, 4500, 1980, 3240, 9624
D 5748, 8748, 3420, 7812;
1956, 5460, 4800, 4728;   9852, 7992
E 5160, 7632, 6252;
4632, 4152, 4908, 9768, 8484

## Page 14 Multiplication – miscellaneous
A 235, 392, 356, 96, 455, 420, 136;
665, 387, 440, 960, 351, 737, 600;
1376, 2094, 5874, 1802, 6096, 2856;
808, 5148, 2786, 4487, 5520, 3655;
8254, 9144, 7360, 6924, 7553;
9344, 9306, 7042, 7082, 7035
B 464, 1708, 4108, 3490
C 3195, 8608, 5556, 8188
D 9018, 582, 1240, 4988, 7854, 8792, 7084

## Page 15 Division – revision
A 333, 333, 222, 111, 111, 222;
92, 51, 61, 51, 31, 71;
172, 192, 151, 161, 161, 181;
191 r 2, 181 r 2, 191 r 2, 141 r 3, 131 r 2,
131 r 2;   213, 119, 119, 114, 327, 239;   287,
162, 156, 486, 144, 194;
108, 209, 109, 309, 109, 409;
112 r 3, 289 r 1, 149 r 3, 254 r 1, 243 r 3,
275 r 1;   170, 150, 140, 190, 160, 130;   330,
210, 230, 110, 130, 410;
200, 200, 200, 300, 200, 400;
176 r 3, 141 r 3, 234 r 2, 150 r 4, 134 r 1,
161 r 2;   197 r 2, 94 r 3, 167 r 1, 335,
88 r 1, 225 r 2
B 95 r 1, 66, 213 r 2;   419 r 1, 255,
232 r 1
C 117 r 2, 324 r 1, 108 r 3, 381 r 1, 144 r 3,
93 r 2

## Page 16 Division – thousands
A 3421, 2112, 2313, 4123, 1321;
418, 311, 642, 311, 421;
912 r 1, 911 r 1, 722 r 2, 832, 611 r 1;
1311 r 2, 1712, 1711 r 1, 3943, 2722 r 1;
1731 r 2, 3781 r 1, 2752 r 2, 1261 r 3,
2391 r 3;   1786 r 1, 262, 1754 r 2,
1569, 1673 r 1;   1094 r 3, 1088, 1093,
3083 r 2, 1097 r 1;   1607 r 3, 1908, 2507,
906, 1307 r 3;   1640 r 3, 4880 r 1,

1470 r 3,  1950 r 2,  1570 r 4;    970 r 2,
909,  2081 r 1,  2068 r 1,  908 r 3;
4017 r 1,  1801 r 1,  3016,  1401,  701;
2007 r 1,  1005,  2009,  1009,  2008 r 2
**B** 623 r 1,  1267 r 1;    1007 r 2,  2080 r 1
**C** 1002, 681, 1500

## Page 17 Division by 7

**A** 2, 7, 3, 9, 0;    5, 8, 1, 4, 6
**B** 6, 6, 6, 5, 5;    6, 4, 3, 2, 6;
4, 5, 1, 5, 5;    4, 4, 2, 6, 3
**C** 7 r 6,  7 r 4,  1 r 5,  8 r 5,  4 r 4;
7 r 3,  4 r 2,  8 r 6,  2 r 6,  4 r 5;
1 r 4,  8 r 4,  7 r 2,  1 r 6,  5 r 5;
7 r 5,  4 r 6,  7 r 1,  5 r 6, 4 r 3
**D** 13 r 4,  12 r 3,  11 r 2,  11 r 6,  13 r 1,
11 r 1,  12 r 5;    19 r 2,  20 r 6,  23 r 3,
21 r 4,  26,  24 r 5;    134 r 5,  58 r 2,  81,
97 r 1,  126 r 2,  51 r 5;    220 r 3,  248 r 3,
280 r 2,  258 r 2, 235 r 5;    900 r 6,
490 r 5,  627,  846 r 6,  395 r 4;
1229 r 4,  1050,  1263 r 5,  1347,  1386 r 5
**E** 610 r 1,  129 r 6,  601 r 3,  205,  127 r 3

## Page 18 Division by 8

**A** 3, 9, 0, 8, 2;    6, 1, 7, 4, 5
**B** 7, 7, 6, 7, 7;    7, 5, 5, 3, 7;
6, 3, 5, 6, 5;    6, 4, 6, 4, 4;    2, 4, 6, 2
**C** 1 r 7,  7 r 7,  6 r 4,  2 r 4,  8 r 7,  3 r 6;
1 r 4,  6 r 6,  7 r 4,  1 r 3,  6 r 5,  8 r 6;
2 r 7,  1 r 2,  6 r 7,  7 r 6,  2 r 6,  6 r 2;
6 r 3,  1 r 6,  7 r 5,  2 r 5,  1 r 5,  3 r 7
**D** 11 r 7,  10 r 7,  12,  11,  11 r 5,  12 r 2,
11 r 1;    18 r 3,  23 r 2,  24,  17 r 6,  13 r 2,
19 r 3;    118 r 2,  121 r 4,  100 r 6,  113 r 5,
124,  119 r 6;    245 r 2,  147 r 3,  236 r 6,  219
r 6,  204;    938 r 2,  791 r 2,  718 r 5,  884,
594;    1112 r 7,  1155 r 3,  1133 r 7,  1093 r 5,
1209 r 1
**E** 540,  1130 r 1,  91 r 1,  211 r 2

## Page 19 Division by 9

**A** 54, 81, 18, 36, 63;    0, 45, 9, 27, 72
**B** 7 r 7,  2 r 8,  5 r 8,  3 r 6,  2 r 5,  4 r 6,
2 r 2;    3 r 3,  1 r 3,  6 r 8,  4 r 7,  8 r 8,
5 r 5,  6 r 6;    1 r 4,  3 r 7,  2 r 3,  1 r 2,
3 r 5,  2 r 4,  1 r 7;    5 r 7,  6 r 7,  5 r 6,
2 r 6,  7 r 8,  4 r 5,  4 r 4;    1 r 5,  2 r 7,
4 r 8,  3 r 8,  1 r 6,  1 r 8,  3 r 4
**C** 11 r 7,  13 r 6,  16,  21 r 3,  15 r 2,
20 r 7;    19 r 4,  16 r 2,  20 r 1,  12 r 2,

22 r 1,  18 r 6;    68 r 7,  91 r 1,  36 r 8,
29 r 3,  75 r 1,  54 r 2;    62 r 5,  44 r 5,
58 r 7,  28 r 3,  85 r 2,  34 r 3;    144 r 5,
141 r 5,  129 r 4,  194 r 4,  182 r 1;
910 r 3,  120 r 3,  157 r 3,  850 r 7,  205 r 3;
671,  255 r 5,  438 r 3,  607 r 3,  730 r 8
**D** 41 r 7, 467 r 4,  438 r 1,  75 r 5;
586 r 5,  89 r 8,  108 r 4,  920;
52,  238,  211  77,  102

## Page 20 Division by 11

**A** 3, 6, 8, 1, 9;    7, 5, 0, 4, 2
**B** 9, 9, 7, 8, 9;    4, 7, 8, 6, 9;    8, 7, 8, 9, 7;
5, 9, 4, 8, 7;    5, 9, 6, 6, 7;    3, 3, 4, 9, 6;
6, 5, 5, 8, 8
**C** 13 r 7,  12 r 9,  15 r 8,  17 r 5,  15,
16 r 10;    61 r 3,  53 r 7,  79,  43 r 9,
30 r 4,  68 r 4;
9 r 4,  9 r 6,  9 r 10,  9 r 9,  9 r 8,  9 r 7;
146 r 1,  180 r 3,  157 r 9,  170,  138 r 7;
659,  200 r 7,  738 r 7,  903 r 3,  410;
97 r 7,  93 r 6,  93 r 7,  96,  96 r 7
**D** 312, 55, 531, 32;    570, 834, 28, 82;
572 r 2,  85 r 7,  200 r 1,  74,  99 r 9

## Page 21 Division by 12

**A** 9, 2, 3, 6, 1;    5, 7, 8, 0, 4
**B** 3 r 7,  4 r 8,  2 r 9,  8 r 8,  6 r 9,  8 r 5;
7 r 6,  3 r 6,  6 r 10,  8 r 6,  4 r 4,  8 r 9;
1 r 8,  7 r 7,  4 r 3,  8 r 4,  6 r 9,  8 r 7;
4 r 7,  3 r 5,  1 r 9,  4 r 2,  4 r 9,  4 r 10;
7 r 9,  7 r 10,  4 r 5,  3 r 10,  7 r 8,  2 r 6;
2 r 8,  3 r 9,  4 r 6,  3 r 4,  6 r 8,  3 r 8
**C** 62 r 5,  57,  31 r 7,  30 r 4,  70 r 11,
77 r 5;    39 r 10,  50 r 7,  80 r 3,  60 r 9,
18,  34 r 6;    9 r 5,  9 r 3,  9 r 4,  9 r 9,  9 r 2,
9 r 7;    170 r 6,  191 r 9,  182 r 8,  184 r 2,
161 r 5;    808 r 8,  627 r 6,  563 r 4,  243 r 5,
398 r 9;    97 r 1,  85 r 4,  89 r 4,  99 r 5,
95 r 10
**D** 601 r 4,  283 r 10,  67 r 4;    600 r 6,  350,
736 r 1;    92 r 7,  33 r 8
**E** 173, 82, 355, 561, 33

## Page 22 Notation

**A** 7 thousands, 7 hundreds, 7 units,
7 tens, 7 units;    7 hundreds, 7 tens,
7 thousands, 7 hundreds, 7 thousands
**B** 6541, 8310, 9743, 9642, 3100;
7710, 9742, 8310, 6532, 7642

**C** three thousand, six hundred and twenty;
seven hundred and fifty;  ninety;
eight hundred and ten;  four thousand,
two hundred and seventy;  eight thousand
and eighty;    five hundred;  four thousand,
six hundred;  five thousand, eight hundred,
nine thousand, six hundred;  seven
thousand, two hundred;    seven hundred;
one thousand, two hundred
**D** thirty-seven;  four,  four hundred and
twenty-seven,  six hundred and thirty-two,
fifty-eight,  seven;   thirty-four,  three,
seventy-one,  eight,  fifty-two
**E** multiply by 10, divide by 10;
divide by 100, multiply by 10;
multiply by 100, divide by 10
**F** 55, 450, 13;    102, 63, 145;
4100, 600, 920;    3200, 1040, 1600

## Page 23 Number series and quotations

**A** 4, 8, **12**, 16, 20, **24**, 28, **32**;
7, 14, 21, 28, **35**, **42**, **49**;
9, 12, **15**, **18**, 21, 24, **27**;
48, **60**, 72, 84, 96, **108**, **120**;
81, 72, 63, **54**, **45**, 36, **27**;
88, 80, 72, **64**, **56**, **48**;
50, **60**, 70, **80**, 90, **100**;
**12**, 14, 16, **18**, 20, 22, **24**;
24, 22, 20, **18**, **16**, **14**;
**100**, 90, **80**, 70, **60**, 50, **40**;
**5**, 10, 15, **20**, **25**, **30**, 35;
32, **28**, 24, **20**, 16, 12, **8**;
66, **55**, 44, 33, **22**, **11**;
55, 66, 77, **88**, **99**, **110**;
24, 32, **40**, **48**, 56, 64, **72**;
**18**, 27, 36, **45**, **54**, 63, 72;
48, 42, **36**, 30, **24**, 18, **12**;
77, **70**, 63, **56**, 49, **42**, 35
**B** 3, 6, 10, 13, 17, **20**, **24**, **27**, **31**;
52, 47, 39, 34, 26, **21**, **13**, **8**, **0**;
2, 8, 10, 16, 18, **24**, **26**, **32**, **34**;
62, 61, 55, 54, 48, **47**, **41**, **40**, **34**
4, 11, 19, 26, 34, **41**, **49**, **56**, **64**;
24, 22, 19, 17, 14, **12**, **9**, **7**, **4**
8, 13, 22, 27, 36, **41**, **50**, **55**, **64**;
54, 50, 43, 39, 32, **28**, **21**, **17**, **10**
**C** 3, 2, 8;    6, 6, 12;    5, 4, 4;    3, 6, 2;
4, 6, 1;    6, 10, 5;    5, 2, 12;    2, 4, 4;
1, 6, 4

## Page 24 Division

**A** 46 r 1,  8 r 1,  15 r 3,  28 r 1,  12 r 6,  9;
7 r 5,  9 r 3,  8 r 1,  8 r 10,  7 r 4,  7 r 8;
365,  248 r 1,  137 r 3,  142 r 2,  229 r 2,  174;
39,  27,  54 r 1,  39 r 2,  68 r 1,  29 r 2;
69 r 9,  93 r 3,  39 r 10,  68 r 2,  83 r 5,
63 r 9;    1494 r 2,  1971 r 1,  2672 r 1,
1913 r 2,  1375 r 4;    151 r 8,  162 r 10,
193 r 6,  126 r 5,  242 r 7;    963 r 2,
907 r 1,  915 r 5,  1572 r 3,  931 r 2;
307, 470, 906, 830, 700;
1007, 1304, 1230, 1052, 3006
**B** 29,  669 r 1,  580,  250,
0 (nothing to add)
**C** 525 r 6,  94 r 3,  133,  181 r 4,  673 r 4,
85 r 5,  601 r 1,  69 r 6

## Page 25 Fractions  – $\frac{1}{2}$ and $\frac{1}{4}$

**A** 1a $\frac{1}{4}$  b $\frac{3}{4}$  2a $\frac{1}{2}$  b $\frac{1}{2}$  3a $\frac{3}{4}$  b $\frac{1}{4}$  4a $\frac{1}{4}$  b $\frac{3}{4}$
**B** D, B;   D, C
**C** 3 cm, 4 $\frac{1}{2}$ cm, 3 cm;    1 $\frac{1}{2}$ cm, 1 $\frac{1}{2}$ cm,
9 cm
**D** 3p, 2, 9p, 10;    4, 12p, 5, 18;
20p, 10, 30, 9
**E** 1, $\frac{1}{2}$, $\frac{3}{4}$, 1;    $\frac{3}{4}$, $\frac{1}{2}$, $\frac{1}{2}$, $\frac{1}{4}$;    1 $\frac{1}{2}$ , 1 $\frac{1}{4}$ , $\frac{3}{4}$ , $\frac{3}{4}$

## Page 26 Fractions – $\frac{1}{8}$

**A** 1a $\frac{1}{8}$   b $\frac{7}{8}$   2a $\frac{5}{8}$   b $\frac{3}{8}$   3a $\frac{7}{8}$   b $\frac{1}{8}$
**4a** $\frac{3}{8}$   b $\frac{5}{8}$
**B** 8, 24, 16, 32
**C** 13, 19, 9, 21
**D** 2, 6, 4, 4
**E** 10, 14, 20, 12
**F** 10, $\frac{5}{8}$, 6, $\frac{1}{4}$
**G** 6, 21, 4, 12;    18, 2, 15, 3;   8, 6, 14, 12

## Page 27 Fractions – $\frac{1}{2}$, $\frac{1}{4}$, $\frac{1}{8}$

**A** F, F, A, F, G;    C, G, G, H, C
**B** 10 cm, 9 cm, 3 cm, 1 cm;    2 $\frac{1}{2}$ cm, 3 cm,
1 cm, 12 cm;    6 cm, 2 cm, 6 cm, 3 cm;
7 cm, 7 cm, 5 cm, 1 cm
**C** 24p, 42, 15 g, 9;    15 cm, 11 $\frac{1}{2}$ cm, 8 cm,
5 $\frac{1}{2}$;    36, 12p, 77, 60 cm;
7p, 12, 15 g, 70 g

## Page 28 Fractions – $\frac{1}{3}$ and $\frac{1}{6}$

**A** 1 $\frac{1}{3}$   2 $\frac{1}{6}$   3 $\frac{2}{3}$   4 $\frac{5}{6}$   5 $\frac{2}{3}$   6 $\frac{5}{6}$
**B** 2, 6, 4;    3, 1, 2;    6, 3
**C** 1 2, 1 2 4, 2 3 4, 2
**D** 4, 6, 2;    10, 8, 12

**Page 29 Fractions – $\frac{1}{2}$, $\frac{1}{3}$, $\frac{1}{4}$, $\frac{1}{6}$, $\frac{1}{8}$**
A 2, 2, 8, 2, 6;   6, 2, 3, 3, 4;   4, 3, 4, 4, 4
B $\frac{1}{8}$, 4;   28, 8, 20;   16, 12
C 30;   15, 25, 10, 20

**Page 30 Fractions – $\frac{1}{5}$ and $\frac{1}{10}$**
A 1a $\frac{2}{5}$ b $\frac{3}{5}$ 2a $\frac{1}{10}$ b $\frac{9}{10}$ 3a $\frac{8}{10}$
b $\frac{2}{10}$ 4a $\frac{7}{10}$ b $\frac{3}{10}$ 5a $\frac{3}{5}$ b $\frac{2}{5}$
6a $\frac{1}{5}$ b $\frac{4}{5}$ 7a $\frac{3}{10}$ b $\frac{7}{10}$ 8a $\frac{9}{10}$ b $\frac{1}{10}$ 9a $\frac{6}{10}$ b $\frac{4}{10}$
B 10, 2, 2, 6, 4;   3, 8, 1, 5, 4;   7, 3, 3, 2;
4, 1, 2, 9
C 5, 63 cm, 4 g, 45;   18p, 28, 18, 84;
18 g, 12p, 72, 27

**Page 31 Fractions**
A 1 $\frac{1}{2}$  2 $\frac{1}{3}$  3 $\frac{1}{6}$  4a 15 b 10 c 5
B 1 $\frac{3}{5}$  2 $\frac{2}{5}$  3 24
C 1 $\frac{1}{4}$  2 $\frac{3}{4}$  3a 15p b 45p
D 1a $\frac{3}{10}$ b $\frac{2}{10}$ ($\frac{1}{5}$) c $\frac{5}{10}$ ($\frac{1}{2}$)
2a 12 b 8 c 20

**Page 32 Decimal notation**
A 1 0·2, 0·5, 0·7, 0·3, 0·6;   0·9, 0·1, 0·4, 0·8
2 0·6, 0·4, 0·3;   0·9, 0·8, 0·5;   0·2, 0·7
3 4·7, 8·3, 2·5, 7·9, 3·4;   1·6, 8·2, 5·8, 6·1
4 8·5, 9·1, 6·2;   3·9, 5·3, 7·4;   9·8, 4·6, 2·7
5 0·15, 0·23, 0·67, 0·21;
0·19, 0·83, 0·52, 0·32
6 0·06, 0·03, 0·08, 0·09;
0·04, 0·07, 0·05, 0·02;   0·01
7 0·11, 0·01, 0·43, 0·29;
0·07, 0·03, 0·09, 0·02;
0·91, 0·88
8 0·19, 0·06;   0·42, 0·09
9 4·07, 9·15, 12·37, 8·09;
11·71, 4·03
10 4·06, 19·15, 52·03, 8·16
B six tenths, six hundredths, nine units, two hundreds;   six hundredths, three tens, two tenths, six units;   one hundred, two tenths, nine hundredths, four tens

**Page 33 Decimal notation**
A 0·4, 7·1, 1·01;   4, 30·2, 18·7;   0·11, 14·2
B 11·10, 11·05, 1·11, 1·10, 1·01, 0·11;
2·01, 1·22, 1·2, 1·12, 1·02, 1·01;
16·32, 16·3, 16·23, 16·2, 16·09, 16·03;
101·99, 101·9, 101·09, 100·99, 100·9, 100·09
C 423, 420·3, 762·7, 858·6, 1432·7
D 2603, 4263, 1805, 20, 57
E 2·46, 9·1, 30·31, 4·2, 27·16

F 32·6, 4·21, 2·02, 34, 20·1
G ÷ 10, ÷ 100, x 10, ÷ 100, ÷ 10
H x 100, ÷ 10, ÷ 10, ÷ 100, x 10

**Page 34 Decimals**
A 20·52, 144·17;   110·17, 13·06;
116·38, 113·66;   235·72, 23·73
B 5·14, 13·73;   8·78, 98·24;
50·34, 5·37;   98·93, 11·05
C 15·8, 1·57;   0·61, 13·63;
5·57, 11·03;   9·13, 104·22
D 24·28, 71·2;   22·83, 34·02;
53·2, 37·31;   43·68, 60·01
E 2·13, 99·13;   5·82, 0·91;
6·67, 8·11;   3·74, 25·93
F 5·7, 33·04, 103·5

**Page 35 Money – composition to £1.00**
A 17p - 2p, 1p  51p - 5p, 2p, 2p;
52p - 5p, 2p, 1p  28p - 2p;
27p - 2p, 1p  69p - 1p;   45p – 1p  82p - 5p, 2p, 1p;   21p - 2p, 2p  21p - 2p, 2p;
62p - 5p, 2p, 1p  33p - 1p;   31p - 5p, 2p, 2p
22p - 2p, 1p;   41p - 2p, 2p  93p - 1p
B 95p, 99p;   87p, 80p;   98p, 97p

**Page 36 Money – composition to £1.00**
A 88p, 76p, 54p, 60p, 47p
B 18p - 10p, 5p, 2p, 1p
15p - 10p, 2p, 2p, 1p
22p - 10p, 10p, 1p, 1p
30p - 10p, 10p, 5p, 5p
16p - 5p, 5p, 5p, 1p
5p - 2p, 1p, 1p, 1p
57p - 50p, 5p, 1p, 1p
75p - 50p, 10p, 10p, 5p;
8p - 5p, 1p, 1p, 1p
35p - 10p, 10p, 10p, 5p
80p - 50p, 10p, 10p, 10p
64p - 50p, 10p, 2p, 2p
19p - 10p, 5p, 2p, 2p
32p - 10p, 10p, 10p, 2p
12p - 5p, 5p, 1p, 1p
9p - 5p, 2p, 1p, 1p
C 43p - 5p, 2p  37p - 10p, 2p, 1p
29p - 20p, 1p  46p - 2p, 2p
22p - 20p, 5p, 2p, 1p  28p - 20p, 2p;
33p - 10p, 5p, 2p  10p - 20p, 20p
38p - 10p, 2p  27p - 20p, 2p, 1p
11p - 20p, 10p, 5p, 2p, 2p  35p - 10p, 5p

**D** 76p - **20p, 2p, 2p**
42p - **50p, 5p, 2p, 1p**   35p - **50p, 10p, 5p**
67p - **20p, 10p, 2p, 1p**   24p - **50p, 20p, 5p,**
**1p**   14p - **50p, 20p, 10p, 5p, 1p**
87p - **10p, 2p, 1p**   93p - **5p, 2p**
**E** Check your child's answers add up to 50p
and £1.00.

## Page 37 Addition and subtraction
**A** 35p, 53p, 44p, 51p, 64p, 82p, 73p;
61p, 70p, 51p, 81p, 94p, 91p, 71p;
81p, 93p, 86p, 87p, 80p, 96p, 81p;
57p, 78p, 83p, 90p, 86p, 89p, 88p
**B** 22p, 33p, 60p, 71p, 82p, 68p, 84p;
28p, 76p, 51p, 77p, 49p, 58p, 70p;
18p, 41p, 33p, 33p, 41p, 5p, 25p;
19p, 26p, 6p, 31p, 49p, 23p, 58p
**C** 98p, 15p, 23p, 98p, 58p, 36p

## Page 38 Multiplication and division
**A** 14p, 24p, 54p;   80p, 36p, 56p;
55p, 27p, 20p;   54p, 88p, 84p;
27p, 96p;   28p, 80p, 63p;   36p, 24p, 40p;
33p, 15p, 24p;   77p, 36p, 36p;
70p, 88p, 57p, 90p, 91p, 92p, 51p;
34p, 84p, 76p, 69p, 64p, 68p
**B** 24p, 9p, 27p, 7p, 14p, 38p, 19p;
21p, 19p, 12p, 13p, 42p, 12p, 18p;
16p, 16p, 12p, 11p, 13p, 27p, 13p
**C 1** 72p **2** 23p **3** 72p **4** 14p **5a** 52p
**b** 78p **c** 39p **d** 91p **e** 26p **6** 18p each

## Page 39 Pounds and pence
**A** 2.00, 5.00, 7.00, 6.00;
9.00, 3.00, 8.00, 4.00
**B** 1.04, 3.05, 1.43;   2.36, 6.24, 3.79;
4.76, 2.17, 9.14;   8.07, 7.63, 2.07
**C** £3.45 = **£3 + 45**p,   £6.17 = **£6 + 17**p;
£7.06 = **£7 + 6**p,   £9.73 = **£9 + 73**p;
£12.14 = **£12 + 14**p,   £15.48 = **£15 + 48**p;
£2.72 = **£2 + 72**p,   £8. 05 = **£8 + 5**p
**D** £4.17 = **417**p,   £8.12 = **812**p,
£9.08 = **908**p;   £8.36 = **836**p,
£6.18 = **618**p,   £3.12 = **312**p,
£2.04 = **204**p,   £5.42 = **542**p;
£5.23 = **523**p,   £6.25 = **625**p,
£4.38 = **438**p,   £4.77 = **477**p
**E** 2+7+2,   6+4+2,   9+0+4,   7+7+2,   8+9+6,
**F** 270, 436, 753, 947, 1036;
92, 34, 25, 67, 83

## Page 40 Pounds and pence
**A** 17p, 27p, 36p, 76p, 89p, 5p
**B** £0.26, £0.07, £0.34, £0.08, £0.52, £0.05
**C** £4.27, £0.76;   £1.18, £0.06;
£2.04, £0.96
**D** seven pounds forty-five,  seventy-two
pence,  fourteen pounds four pence,
three pounds sixty-two;   twelve pence,
five pounds thirty-two,  nine pounds
twenty-six,  seven pence
**E** £4.36, 414p, £4.00, 47p, £0.44;
£5.50, £5.27, 505p, £0.61, 59p;
£22.00, £2.20, £2.02, 200p, 22p
**F** £1.09, £1.21, £1.16, £0.92, £1.29, £1.10;
£0.70, £1.21, £1.15, £1.03, £0.99, £1.16

## Page 41 Addition and subtraction – £.p
**A** £0.60, £0.85, £0.89, £0.82, £0.88;
£1.06, £1.26, £1.33, £1.30, £1.23;
£6.73, £9.00, £9.39, £9.99, £13.03;
£8.46, £7.04, £10.63, £10.21, £18.02
**B** £0.05, £0.13, £0.28, £0.17, £0.29;
£1.16, £0.60, £0.86, £0.63, £0.57;
£2.08, £3.51, £3.00, £0.79, £1.03
**C** £7.05, £2.78, £16.65, £6.08, £7.24, £15.52

## Page 42 Multiplication – £.p
**A** £0.90, £0.96, £0.96, £0.94, £0.90;
£0.95, £0.84, £0.91, £0.81, £0.88;
£4.24, £4.56, £3.80, £3.12, £5.76;
£2.88, £3.35, £6.51, £2.86, £3.84;
£17.16, £27.60, £24.56, £38.88, £9.54;   £6.21,
£7.44, £ 22.26, £12.86, £44.91
**B** £12.66, £23.38;   £19.02, £109.44;   £19.62,
£101.16
**C** £25.38, £17.60
**D** £96.48, £27.78
**E** £8.13, £0.81

## Page 43 Division – £.p
**A** £0.06, £0.24, £0.14, £0.17, £0.29;
£0.07, £0.12, £0.10, £0.46, £0.06;
£0.12, £0.13, £0.09, £0.07, £0.26;
£0.16, £0.23, £0.47, £0.12, £0.22;
£0.26, £0.17, £0.15, £0.18, £0.32;
£0.44, £0.17, £0.38, £0.22, £0.25;
£4.36, £1.81, £1.39, £0.61, £1.20;
£2.70, £3.17, £5.62, £3.93, £2.19;
£4.90, £3.83, £2.87, £3.16, £2.81

B £0.96, £0.68; £11.03, £9.41;
£0.39, £4.02; £0.76, £3.01;
£6.70, £6.04
C £4.72, £2.32;   £0.92, £0.34;
£12.03, £10.71

## Page 44 The toy shop
1 £1.40 **2** £7.16 **3a** 28p **b** 25p **c** 55p
4 £4.55 **5** £10.50 **6a** £5.00 **b** £6.66
**c** £2.88 **d** £3.25 **e** £2.10 **7** £1.77 **8** £2.58
9 6 kites, 10p change **10** 3 aeroplanes, £1.66

## Page 45 Capacity
**A 1** 1000 ml, 2000 ml, 4000 ml, 6000 ml;
9000 ml, 7000 ml, 3000 ml, 5000 ml;
500 ml, 250 ml, 1500 ml, 1250 ml;
750 ml, 2250 ml, 2750 ml, 1750 ml
**2** 500 ml, 400 ml, 900 ml, 700 ml;
300 ml, 800 ml, 200 ml, 100 ml;
2400 ml, 1600 ml, 3800 ml, 4500 ml;
6100 ml, 5300 ml, 8800 ml, 2700 ml
**B** Check your child's answers all add
up to 1 litre.
**C** Check your child's answers all add
up to 500 ml.
**D 1** medicine and small milk **2** 4 bottles
**3** lemonade and pop **4** 125 ml **5** 3
**6** small milk, pop and wine

## Page 46 Length – m and cm
**A** 200 cm, 900 cm, 600 cm, 400 cm,
700 cm;   1200 cm, 1600 cm
**B** 4 m, 3 m, 5 m, 1 m, 8 m;   13 m
**C** 50, 25, 75;   250, 125, 175;
450, 225, 275;   650, 425, 775
**D** $\frac{1}{2}$, $\frac{1}{2}$, $\frac{3}{4}$;   $3\frac{1}{2}$, $5\frac{1}{4}$, $3\frac{3}{4}$;   $1\frac{1}{2}$, $3\frac{1}{4}$, $4\frac{3}{4}$
**E** 123, 216;   405, 308;   936, 829
**F 2** m **25** cm, **5** m **18** cm;   **3** m **12** cm,
**6** m **54** cm;   **8** m **6** cm, **9** m **31** cm
**G** 5·32 m, 1·96 m, 0·92 m;
4·02 m, 0·52 m, 3·07 m;
3·9 m, 0·07 m, 14·26 m;
426 Cm, 816 cm, 1027 cm;
1206 cm, 9 cm, 341 cm;   27 cm, 77 cm,
101 cm
**H** 0·5 m, 0·25 m, 0·75 m, 0·01 m, 0·23 m;
0·47 m, 1·11 m, 2·29 m

## Page 47 Length – m, cm and mm
**A** 5 cm, 4 cm, 6 cm;   3 cm, 9 cm, 2 cm;
13 cm, 22 cm, 19 cm

B 70 mm, 80 mm, 90 mm;   60 mm, 50 mm,
30 mm;   150 mm, 3200 mm, 5300 mm
**C** 53 mm = **5** cm **3** mm = **5·3** cm,
7 mm = **0** cm **7** mm = **0·7** cm;
86 mm = **8** cm **6** mm = **8·6** cm,
4 mm = **0** cm **4** mm = **0·4** cm;
131 mm = **13** cm **1** mm = **13·1** cm,
6 mm = **0** cm **6** mm = **0·6** cm;
268 mm = **26** cm **8** mm = **26·8** cm,
320 mm = **32** cm **0** mm = **32** cm
**D** 41 mm, 37 mm, 9 mm, 8 mm;
142 mm, 56 mm
**E** 7·000 m, 9·000 m, 3·000 m;   4·500 m,
2·500 m, 8·500 m;   5·250 m, 8·250 m,
1·250 m;   9·750 m, 3·750 m, 4·750 m
**F** 6500 mm, 5500 mm, 3500 mm, 2750 mm;
1750 mm, 4250 mm, 7250 mm, 9250 mm
**G** 6670 mm = **6** m **670** mm,   5026 mm =
**5** m **26** mm,   2340 mm = **2** m **340** mm;
8026 mm = **8** m **26** mm,   2726 mm = **2** m
**726** mm,   8791 mm = **8** m **791** mm;
**H** 4 m 135 mm = **4135** mm,
6 m 296 mm = **6296** mm,
8 m 196 mm = **8196** mm,
16 m 176 mm = **16 176** mm,
5 m 17 mm = **5017** mm,
9 m 5 mm = **9005** mm

## Page 48 The kilometre
**A** 1275 m, 3536 m, 4326 m;
8824 m, 2056 m, 7036 m;
5004 m, 6008 m, 4500 m, 3250 m;
2750 m, 9500 m
**B** 3 km 760 m,  2 km 430 m,  1 km 641 m;
8 km 252 m,  5 km 862 m, 4 km 26 m;
7 km 54 m, 1 km 6 m, 3 km 2 m, 6 km 8 m

## Perimeter
**C A a** 7·5 cm **b** 2·5 cm **c** 20 cm,
**B a** 4·5 cm **b** 4·5 cm **c** 18 cm,
**C a** 3·5 cm **b** 2 cm **c** 11 cm, **D a** 6 cm
**b** 2·5 cm **c** 17 cm, **E a** 7 cm **b** 2·5 cm
**c** 19 cm, **F a** 5·5 cm **b** 4·5 cm **c** 20 cm,
**G a** 5·5 cm **b** 1·5 cm **c** 14 cm

## Page 49 Area
**A A** 15 cm$^2$, **B** 8 cm$^2$, **C** 9 cm$^2$,
**D** 17 cm$^2$, **E** 29 cm$^2$, **F** 13·5 cm$^2$,
**G** 9 cm$^2$
**B A** 24 cm$^2$, **B** 6 cm$^2$, **C** 18 cm$^2$,
**D** 4 cm$^2$, **E** 16 cm$^2$

**Page 50 Area and perimeter**
A **a** 27 cm **b** 38 cm², B **a** 17 cm
**b** 17·5 cm², C **a** 15 cm **b** 12·5 cm²,
D **a** 21 cm **b** 17 cm², E **a** 27 cm
**b** 31·5 cm², F **a** 17 cm **b** 15 cm²,
G **a** 19 cm **b** 17·5 cm², H **a** 15 cm
**b** 6·5 cm², I **a** 18 cm **b** 18 cm²

**Page 51 Scale measurement**
A **1** 20 cm **2** 4 cm **3** 11 cm **4** 8 cm
**5** 16 cm **6** 9 cm
B 10 cm, 15 cm, 9 cm, 7 cm, 3 cm;
6 cm
C 30 cm, 45 cm, 65 cm, 55 cm, 70 cm
D 4·5 cm, 6 cm, 5·5 cm, 2 cm, 5 cm;
2·5 cm
E 48 km

**Page 52 Scales and maps**
A **1** 150 km **2** 100 km;
**3** 60 km **4** 30 km; **5** 50 km **6** 60 km;
**7** 160 km **8** 70 km; **9** 220 km **10** 120 km;
**11** 70 km **12** 60 km
B 42·5 km, 55 km, 62·5 km, 22·5 km,
65 km; 3 cm, 8 cm, 5 cm, 12 cm, 3·5 cm;
10·5 cm
C 1 cm to 1 m, 1 cm to ½ km, 1 cm to ⅕ km,
1 cm to ¼ m, 1 cm to ⅓ km

**Page 53 Mass**
A 500 g **a** 10 **b** 4; 200 g **a** 25 **b** 10;
100 g **a** 50 **b** 20; 50 g **a** 100 **b** 40;
20 g **a** 250 **b** 100; 10 g **a** 500 **b** 200
B 2000 g, 8500 g, 6500 g, 10 000 g;
3500 g, 7000 g
C 4 kg, 6 kg, 8·5 kg, 2·5 kg; 5 kg, 3·5 kg
D 4 kg 260 g, 8 kg 120 g, 2 kg 50 g;
3 kg 160 g, 7 kg 5 g
E 2360 g, 3115 g, 5070 g; 4033 g, 6005 g
F 3200 g, 4100 g, 6300 g, 5400 g; 8600 g
G 64 g, 271 g, 153 g, 209 g, 468 g; 433 g
H 1 kg 471 g, 126 g, 2 kg 21 g;
9 kg 741 g, 6 kg 6 g
I 1 kg 750 g, 1 kg 400 g, 1 kg 100 g, 5 kg
500 g, 50 g

**Page 54 Comparison – other measures**
**1** 300 oranges **2** 287·5 l **3** 6 lengths :
20 cm left **4** 5·4 l **5** 3·65 kg **6** 34 packs
**7** 4·5 m **8** 58 l **9** 250 bottles **10** 100 bags
**11** 25 bags **12** 8·4 l **13** 1·36 m (136 cm)

**14** 4 lengths **15** 1·7 kg **16** 200 steps
**17** 1·050 kg **18** 60 doses **19** 1·5 kg
**20a** 33 **b** 4 cm

**Page 55 Shopping**
**1a** £3.20 **b** £4.80 **c** £8.00 **d** £7.20
**2a** 5p **b** 25p **c** 90p **d** £1.20
**3a** 8p **b** 48p **c** 56p **d** 72p
**4a** 90p **b** 40 p **c** 45p **d** 75p
**5a** 80p **b** 96p **c** 8p **d** 40p
**6a** 45p **b** 30p **c** £2.55 **d** £1.65
**7a** £12.50 **b** £21.25 **c** £15.00 **d** £8.75
**8a** 30p **b** £2.70 **c** £4.20 **d** £6.00
**9a** £2.88 **b** £2.40 **c** £4.80 **d** £6.72
**10a** 48p **b** 24p **c** £1.20 **d** £1.56
**11a** 11p **b** 44p **c** £2.42 **d** 99p
**12a** £6.30 **b** £1.75 **c** £4.20 **d** £8.40
**13a** £1.75 **b** £1.05 **c** £2.45 **d** £3.50
**14a** 8p **b** £1.76 **c** £2.00 **d** £2.24
**15a** 5p **b** 35p **c** 45p **d** 15p
**16a** 28p **b** 42p **c** 63p **d** £1.12
**17a** 24p **b** 30p **c** 60p **d** 75p
**18a** 40p **b** 16p **c** 28p **d** £2.20

**Page 56 Time – revision**
A 5 past 2, 20 past 7, 12 o'clock,
25 past 4, 20 past 11; ½ past 1, 10 past 5, 10
past 9, ¼ past 6, 25 past 10
B 25 to 10, 35 min past 9; 5 to 8, 55 min
past 7; 20 to 5, 40 min past 4;
10 to 2, 50 min past 1; ¼ to 4, 45 min past 3;
5 to 12, 55 min past 11; ¼ to 2, 45 min past
1; 20 to 1, 40 min past 12; 10 to 3, 50
min past 2; 25 to 9, 35 min past 8
C Check that your child's clocks show the
correct times.

**Page 57 Time – am and pm**
A 6:10, 8:45, 3:50; 8:15, 4:40, 9:55
B 1:20, 12:05, 6:55, 2:25, 3:35
C 2:15 am, 9:35 am, 6:45 am, 4:10 am,
8:20 am; 11:50 pm, 3:30 pm, 5:40 pm,
11:25 pm, 8:55 pm
D 12:35 pm, 6:20 pm, 3:50 am, 7:45 pm,
12:25 am, 8:55 pm, 2:15 am, 11:10 pm,
3:05 pm; 5:30 am

**Page 58 Time in minutes**
A **a** 4 min **b** 8 min **c** 11 min **d** 19 min
**e** 22 min **f** 28 min **g** 32 min **h** 39 min
**i** 43 min **j** 49 min **k** 53 min **l** 56 min

**B** 12:08, 2:38, 5:24, 6:49;
10:42, 11:48, 2:03, 8:26
**C** 7:44 am, 4:59 pm, 1:17 pm, 10:29 am

## Page 59 Adjusting times
**A** 2:05, 12:09, 8:01, 4:06
**B** 6:56, 4:59, 7:52, 6:02
**C** 30 min, 19 min, 2 min, 6 min
**D** 25 min, 15 min;  40 min, 20 min;
45 min, 5 min

## Page 60 Time – problems
**A 1** 1 h 40 min **2** 24 min **3** 42 min
**4** 1 h 5 min **5** Benford to Markham
**6** Southam to Fartown
**B** 2 h 30 min, 30 min;
19 min, 22 min;  1 h 13 min, 43 min;
1 h 55 min, 2 h 21 min
**C** 90 min, 75 min, 150 min, 270 min;
105 min, 135 min, 165 min
**D** 6:25 pm
**E** 3:10
**F** 8 min
**G 1** 75 min **2** 3:45 pm

## Page 61 The calendar
**1** No, as February has 28 days, not 29
**2** March, June, August, November

**3** April, July **4** March, June **5** June
**6** 20 June
**7** 13 January, 10 February, 10 March,
14 April, 12 May, 9 June, 14 July,
11 August, 8 September, 13 October,
10 November, 8 December
**8** January – Wednesday, March – Saturday,
May – Thursday, July – Tuesday, August –
Friday, October – Wednesday, December –
Monday
**9** April – Sunday, June – Friday, September
– Saturday, November – Thursday
**10** Monday **11** Tuesday **12** Tuesday

## Page 62 Graphs
**A** 35, 36, 30, 35, 26, 32
**1** History **2** French **3** Geography and Maths
**4** Science **5** 10 **6** 240 **7** 194 **8** 46
**B** 17, 34, 41, 36, 43, 21
**1** 98 **2** 94 **3** 192 **4** 8 **5** football **6** netball
**7** 64 **8** 53 **9** hockey **10** 4

## Page 63 Graphs
**A 1** Heaton **2** Birford **3** Wessex and Frame
**4** Birford and Imford **5** 8 **6** Heaton and
Birford
**B 1** 180 **2** 19 **3** class 4 **4** class 1
**C**

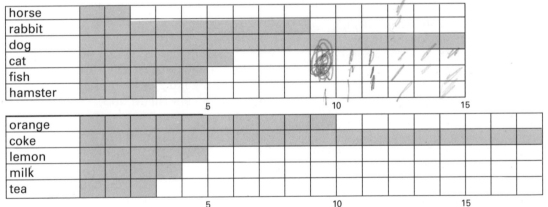